629.225
    Buf
Buff, Sheila
    Fire engines

04/7
'17

OCT. 0 2 1996

629.225
    Buf
Buff, Sheila
    Fire engines

JAN 8   95          AL 59643
FEB 26 95           AL 66241
JUL 31 95           SB 6630
OCT 2   96          SB 6513
OCT 30 96           SB 6513
NOV 20 96
FEB 2   97          SB 5917A

MAY 23 97           SB 6513
SEP 5   96          XX 32026

# FIRE ENGINES

## *Motorized Apparatus Since 1900*

*The Chicago Fire Department created some weirdly huge water delivery systems. Shown here is the famous "Big John" turret wagon. This rear view of "Big John" in action shows the numerous inlets needed to feed the giant turret nozzles.*

# FIRE ENGINES

*Motorized Apparatus*
*Since 1900*

## SHEILA BUFF

LONGMEADOW
PRESS

Copyright © 1994 Sheila Buff.

Published by Longmeadow Press
201 High Ridge Road
Stamford, CT 06904

Produced by Benford Books, Inc.
28 Benford Drive
Princeton Junction, NJ 08550

Design: Tony Meisel
Origination and Printing: Cronion, S.A., Barcelona

ISBN: 0-691-00545-9

Printed in Spain

First Longmeadow Edition

0 9 8 7 6 5 4 3 2 1

12/14/94        629.225 BuF      14.98

# Contents

*The locomotive influence is clear in this engraving of a self-propelling steam engine, the* J.C. Cary, *demonstrated in New York City in 1858.*

FIRE ENGINES

# Chapter One

# Prelude to the Automobile

Although steam power, in the form of locomotives and stationary engines, had taken hold by the early decades of the nineteenth century, firefighting apparatus of the period was still powered by humans. Well-organized volunteer fire brigades existed in most municipalities. Although horses provided the main motive power for other forms of transport—and since 1802 even for some fire companies—the volunteers of this period still insisted on pulling their apparatus to fires themselves. Once at the fire scene, they pumped their engines manually, an exhausting and often dangerous procedure. Hand pumpers could generate surprisingly high pressures, at least in short spurts, but they still needed to be positioned very close to the flames. Few hand pumpers survive today, in part because so many were lost to flames and collapsing walls.

The proud volunteers of the period found it hard to admit that their efforts could be improved upon, but by the 1830s some forward-thinking engineers were experimenting with steam-powered fire engines. In London, John Braithwaite was demonstrating steam-powered pumps for firefighting and was finding limited acceptance. For the fire service as for the rest of a rapidly industrializing world, the quest was on for ways to replace human and animal labor with efficient, untiring, uncomplaining machinery.

## SELF-PROPELLED STEAMERS

By 1835, the locomotive age was well under way in the United States, with some 175 locomotives in service. The locomotive model provided the basis for one school of thought regarding steam-powered fire engines: self-propelled steam engines. Although this approach became no more than an occasionally bizarre detour on the road to the automotive fire engine, it produced some extremely interesting apparatus.

In the United States, the first experiment in self-propelled steam got under way in 1840. An English-born engineer, Paul Rapsey Hodge, was commissioned by a coalition of New York City insurance companies to build a powerful steam fire engine. Hodge had been trained as a railway engineer, so it was natural that his fire engine design was, in effect, a locomotive. The huge apparatus was $13\frac{1}{2}$ feet long and weighed over 14,000 pounds. Christened *Exterminator*, it was demonstrated to the public in front of City Hall in New York on 27 March 1841. The large wrought iron drive wheels at the rear were driven by piston rods connected to the double-acting horizontal pumps, which were bolted directly onto the cylinders. The apparatus had a large horizontal boiler, a smokestack, and small front wheels for steering. In operation, the rear wheels were jacked up to act as flywheels. After taking about half an hour to get up enough steam, the *Exterminator* did manage to shoot a stream 166 feet high.

Unimpressed, no engine company in New York wanted to accept the machine for a trial. It was finally taken by the Pearl Hose Company No. 28, in the Fifth District. Unenthusiastic from the start, the volunteers quickly developed a long list of complaints about the engine's slowness and difficulty of maintenance. Other volunteer companies wanted nothing to do with such newfangled machinery and refused to supply water to it. The experiment ended unsuccessfully a few months later. *Exterminator* was returned to the insurance companies with insincere thanks. It ended its days ignominiously as a stationary engine for a box manufacturer.

This abortive experiment in self-propelled steam failed for two main reasons. First, it took far too long for the engine to get up enough steam to move. Second, the apparatus was so heavy that it when it did get going, it moved very slowly. The problem of raising steam quickly is one that later designers of steam engines were able to overcome quite effectively. The question of weight was a far trickier issue, one that was never really solved for self-propelled apparatus.

After the *Exterminator* experience, the idea of steam-powered fire apparatus languished for more than a decade. In 1853, however, two entrepreneurs in Cincinnati came up with an idea for a fire engine with a steam-powered pump. One partner in the venture was Alexander Bonner Latta, who had built and operated the first railroad locomotive west of the Alleghenies. The other partner was Abel Shawk, an expert machinist. Shawk had found a way to solve the steam-raising problem by designing a new copper coil that enabled his steam engine to raise steam in under five minutes. At its first public demonstration, the Latta and Shawk fire engine threw a stream 130 feet through 350 feet of hose. The city council, led by Joseph Ross, appropriated $5,000 to buy a steam fire engine from the new firm.

Alexander Latta's experience with trains led him to build a self-propelled fire engine that looked and operated a lot like a locomotive. The design used two steam cylinders coupled to the two rear wheels, driving them in exactly the same way as a locomotive. When the rear drive was disengaged, the steam cylinders drove the double pumps. Steering was accomplished by a single wheel in the front. Called the *Joseph Ross* after its patron (and more familiarly known as the *Uncle Joe Ross*), this behemoth was actually only partially self-propelled. At 22,000 pounds, it was so heavy that a team of four horses was needed to pull it along as it raised steam. Even with the steam raised and the self-propelling gear engaged, the horses were still needed, especially when going uphill.

The new engine was demonstrated on 1 January 1853 in a competition against the most powerful hand engine in Cincinnati. Long before the engine arrived at the contest site, it could be heard rumbling over the cobblestones. By the time it finally got there, twenty

The original idea of a steam-powered, self-propelled fire engine probably came from observing railroad operations. In this photo, a Union Pacific Railroad crew in the early 1860s demonstrates how the steam-powered water pump on the locomotive can be used to fight fires. This locomotive was wrecked in an Indian raid in 1867.

A successor to the Uncle Joe Ross was a 9,000-pound self-propelled steamer built by A.B. Latta. Purchased from money donated by residents, it was christened Citizens' Gift.

This 1906 gasoline-powered, hand-drawn pump was built by Waterous in 1906. This little rig was the first motorized apparatus in California; it is still owned by the Suisun City department. The 6-cylinder motor is rated at 48 horsepower and pumps 300 gpm.

FIRE ENGINES

*Engine 38, a self-propelled steam engine built by the Manchester Locomotive Works (successor to Amoskeag) in 1897, served in Boston for almost thirty years. Maximum pumping capacity was 1,350 gpm.*

*Hartford's famous Jumbo lets off steam for the photographer in this shot from 1901. Built by Amoskeag in 1889, Jumbo weighed over five tons and was the world's largest steam fire engine. Despite a differential gear and cleats on the rear wheels, Jumbo tended to skid. In snowy weather, the steering wheel was removed and horses were hitched to the rig.*

FIRE ENGINES

minutes after leaving its engine house, the volunteers had already arrived, set up, and begun pumping their Hunneman engine. Their best efforts produced a 200-foot stream.

The volunteers were in for a nasty shock. When the *Uncle Joe* was finally ready for action, it pumped a powerful 225-foot stream. The volunteers gave up in exhaustion half an hour later without bettering their stream, but the *Uncle Joe* kept on pumping steadily and with undiminished strength, even with six streams working.

The end had come for the volunteers in Cincinnati. On 10 March 1853 the city council voted to start a paid fire department on 1 April of that year. The Cincinnati department became the first salaried fire department in America.

Alexander Latta, by now working alone, delivered a second self-propelled steamer to Cincinnati in 1854. Called the *Citizens' Gift*, this apparatus also was ostensibly self-propelled, but it still needed a complement of four horses to move it around. Latta seems to have made some design improvements. During one demonstration, the apparatus was able to arrive at a site about a quarter mile from the engine house and begin pumping within six minutes from a cold start.

The self-propelled concept still had major drawbacks. One problem was that the *Citizens's Gift* still needed four horses and ten men to operate it. Another was cost: $13,400. Yet another was reliability and safety. The boiler of the *Uncle Joe Ross* exploded in 1854, killing the engineer. Alexander Latta continued to tinker with the design of his self-propelled steamers. By 1860 he had built some 30 rigs, but by 1862 he had retired from business; he died in 1865.

Rapid improvements in horse-drawn

steam fire engines meant that there was little demand for self-propelled apparatus. Even so, hard-headed businessmen and crackpots alike continued the search for self-propulsion.

## AMOSKEAG SELF-PROPELLERS

By the 1860s Amoskeag-type steam fire engines, made by the Manchester Locomotive Works of New Hampshire, had emerged as the standard by which others were judged. The company was a consistent innovator in the field. Among the more interesting Amoskeag developments were 22 massively powerful self-propelled steamers built between 1868 and 1908. The demonstrator model, built in 1868, was sold to New York in 1872. On a good road, it could get up to an amazing ten miles an hour. Another of Amoskeag's early self-propellers was sold to Boston in 1872. These behemoths had a serious flaw, however: the chain drive used for power transmission to the rear wheels was located on one side of the engine. This led to serious steering difficulties, particularly when going around corners, because both rear wheels rotated at the same speed, causing the rig to skid. The solution was the invention of the differential gear—the first use of a differential gear on a self-propelled vehicle. The four additional Amoskeag self-propellers purchased by New York in 1874 had differentials.

Driving an Amoskeag self-propeller was a two-man operation. The engineer stood on the fuel pan behind the boiler and operated the throttle to provide power; the driver sat in front, controlled the brakes, and wrestled with the enormous, vertically mounted steering wheel. The pumping capacity of an Amoskeag self-propeller was a fairly impressive 1,450 gallons per minute.

Amoskeag sold a self-propeller to

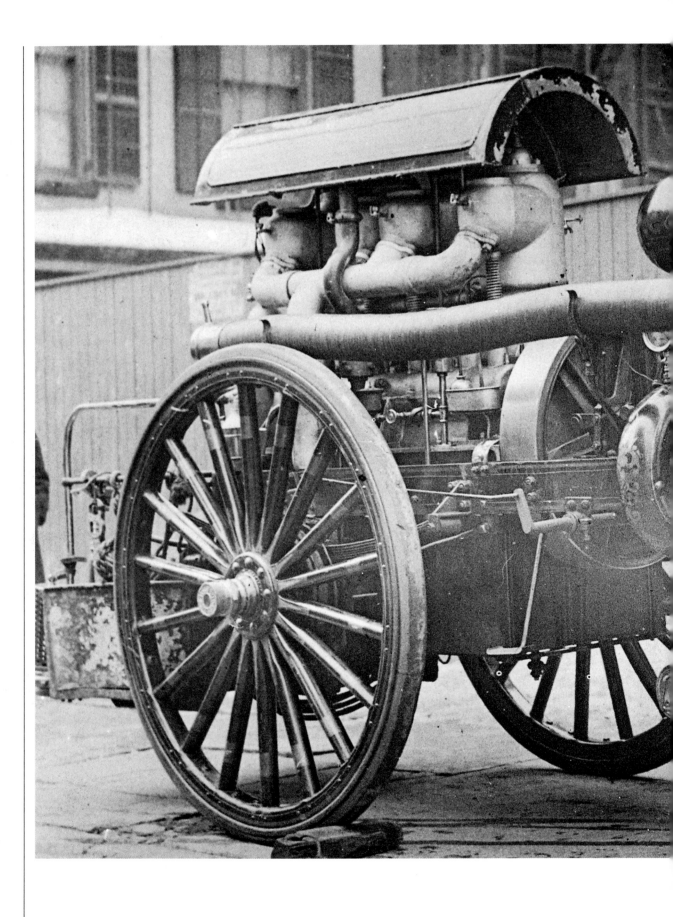

Westinghouse built this gasoline-powered, horse-drawn pump for FD.NY in 1910. The pump was powered by a 4-cylinder, 4-cycle engine; it put out 500 gpm. A few of these models were sold elsewhere, but they were never more than experimental.

Brooklyn in 1874; other units went to Boston, Hartford, Detroit, Portland, Chicago, Vancouver, Pittsburgh, and elsewhere. One of the best-known of these engines was the 5½-ton vehicle sold to Hartford in 1889. At the time it was the largest fire engine in the world, and became something of a tourist attraction. At full throttle, this ponderous rig, aptly nicknamed *Jumbo*, could get up to 25 miles an hour, generating about 100 horsepower. In acceptance trials, the pump threw a horizontal stream 348 feet through 50 feet of 3½-inch hose with a 1½-inch nozzle.

The Amoskeag sold to Boston in 1897 was another giant. It was 10 feet tall, 16½ feet long, seven feet, three inches wide, and weighed in at 17,000 pounds. On average, this engine could pump 870 gallons per minute, although rates of up 1,500 gallons of minute were recorded for self-propellers.

Hartford's *Jumbo* remained in service for more than 30 years. It was then converted to motor power by having a tractor attached to it; thus modified, it continued in service for several more years. The four self-propelled steamers in New York were taken out of service in 1884, while the one in use in Brooklyn lasted until 1892. In 1908, seven self-propellers remained in service in other cities. The last Amoskeag self-propeller was sold to Vancouver in 1908 for $12,500. It stayed in use into the 1940s.

Clumsy, expensive, inefficient, and even dangerous (the sparks from the smokestack sometimes started fires, and having the throttle controlled by one operator and the brakes by another was a recipe for frequent near-disasters), self-propellers were nonetheless fairly cost effective. Officials in New Orleans in 1901 calculated that monthly operating costs for their self-propeller were $27 a month, compared to $60 a month for a steamer drawn by three horses.

Experiments with self-propelled steam engines continued now and again even after the gasoline engine had proven its superiority. The results were decidedly mixed. In 1901, for example, an English horse-drawn steam engine was converted to self-propulsion. The modified apparatus could get up steam in about five minutes, traveled at 12 miles an hour on a level road, and could climb steep hills without assistance. Despite these advantages, the apparatus was unpopular, perhaps because on one of its earliest runs sparks from the smokestack ignited a wagonload of hay and started several fires in hedges and haystacks en route to the fire scene. Once at the fire, a pipe in the engine burst, rendering it inoperable. Another steam-powered engine went into service in England at Battersea in 1903. The 25 horsepower engine could get the apparatus up to 30 miles an hour. Interestingly, the boiler was fueled by petroleum, not coal.

In France, the city of Paris experimented with an automobile steam fire engine in 1904. This apparatus was rated at 30 horsepower and could achieve a speed of nearly 15 miles an hour. In addition to the pump, this rig carried suction pipes, hose, 50 gallons of water, 265 pounds of coal, and a crew of twelve.

The last gasp of steam self-propulsion came from American LaFrance. Between 1903 and 1907 the firm delivered several steam-powered vehicles. The best-known apparatus was a steam-powered combination hose and chemical car delivered to the Niagara Fire Co. No. 1 of New London, Connecticut, in 1904. The propulsion was supplied by two individual steam engines geared to the rear wheels.

## HORSE-DRAWN GASOLINE PUMPERS

Gasoline-powered stationary engines were being developed alongside the automobile. A few pump manufacturers came up with the idea of gasoline-powered pumpers on horse-drawn chassis. In the early years of the twentieth century, Waterous, Howe, and Westinghouse provided variations on this concept. New York City received a 4-cylinder, 4-cycle gasoline pump from Westinghouse in 1910. The pump had a capacity of 500 gpm. Howe Fire Apparatus produced a number of horse-drawn gasoline-powered pumps that were fairly popular with rural areas as a cheaper and lighter alternative to steam pumpers. These engine were available in a vareity of configurations, including a choice of rotary or piston pump. The Waterous Engine Works, based in St. Paul, Minnesota, also produced horse-drawn gasoline pumps. These 6-cylinder pumps were rated at 48 horsepower and put out a respectable 300 to 350 gpm.

*Early experiments with gasoline-powered fire engines followed the steam engine model, using the engine only for pumping; propulsion came from humans or horses. The first ever gasoline-driven fire pump was this one, built by Waterous in 1898. This pump could be drawn by hand or horse. It delivered 175 gpm.*

*The latest in fire-fighting apparatus, circa 1896, was this quadricycle used by the Paris fire department. The quadricycle carried a hose reel mounted between the two front riders; a pump was mounted below and behind the rear riders.*

## ANOTHER APPROACH TO SELF-PROPULSION

The introduction in 1887 of the safety bicycle, with its wheels of equal size, sturdy triangular frame, and chain drive, started a genuine bicycle craze among the American public. By 1895, 1.2 million bicycles were being produced every year. Enterprising young men such as Orville and Wilbur Wright were going into the bicycle business. Naturally, proposals for bicycles in firefighting were common. In 1899, for example, the fire commissioner of Washington, D.C. proposed sending out a fireman on bicycle, with a chemical fire extinguisher strapped to his back, ahead of the squad. Another proposal for the District of Columbia department was a duplex bicycle carrying a large chemical tank, scaling ladder, and pick, to be propelled by two firemen. This idea may have been derived from a French experiment of 1896 that had four firemen pedalling to the fire on a quadricycle fitted with a pump.

Harebrained as these ideas sound today, it must be remembered that the bicycle in the 1890s created the first real public demand for personal transportation—a demand that the automobile would begin to fill a decade or so later. In addition, the technology involved in the mass production of bicycles was a prelude to that applied to cars later on: electrical welding, ball bearings, chain and shaft transmissions, metal stamping techniques, and rubber tires. And just as would happen in the automobile industry later on, the number of manufacturers jumped rapidly, going from 27 in 1890 to 312 in 1897 and then dropping off sharply after 1900 as the bicycle craze gave way to the automobile age.

*Upon arrival at the fire, the Parisian bicycle firemen attached their pump to the hydrant and began pedalling the quadricycle to power it. At that point, the fifth fireman magically appeared and acted as hose man. Not one of the best ideas to ever come to the fire service, the quadricycle failed to cross the Atlantic.*

# Chapter Two

# The Automotive Age Begins

The perfection of a four-stroke, gasoline-powered, internal-combustion engine by the German engineer Nikolaus August Otto in the 1870s was an achievement with immense consequences. Otto's invention was patented in 1877. By 1885 his engine was being used to propel purpose-built vehicles which quickly came to be known as automobiles. Although much of the development work was done in Europe, by the 1890s automobiles were starting to appear on American roads. The first commercial automobiles in the United States were made by the Duryea brothers—bicycle mechanics from Springfield, Massachusetts—in 1896.

The automobile led to massive changes in the landscape, economy, and society of the United States—and not a minute too soon. Large cities were being overwhelmed by the huge numbers of horses needed for transportation. Just the maintenance requirements of the horses—hay, grain, water, stables— added to the congestion. The problem of waste disposal was growing increasingly acute. By the late 1800s, two-thirds of the municipal waste in a typical American city was horse-related. Banks of horse manure several feet high lined

some slum streets in Manhattan in the 1880s. An estimate from around 1900 claimed that 2.5 million pounds of manure were deposited on the streets of New York every day. The horses themselves were often dreadfully ill-treated and frequently died in harness—on average, 15,000 horses a year died in New York City at the turn of the century. Disposal of the bodies was an additional burden on municipal sanitation.

Laughable as it seems today, the coming of the automobile markedly reduced congestion and filth in cities. Millions of acres of agricultural land once devoted to raising horses and growing fodder for them could be put to other uses, such as the suburban houses buyers demanded once the automobile made commuting to work possible.

## EARLY AUTOMOBILES IN THE FIRE SERVICE

By the time the hand pumper manned by volunteers had reached its highest possible level of efficiency, it was superseded by the invention of the steam pumper and the move to professional fire departments. The transition in the 1860s and 1870s was a painful experience for

tradition-bound volunteers.

By the start of the twentieth century, the horse-drawn steam fire engine manned by paid professionals had also reached a maximal level of efficiency. Even so, considerable drawbacks to the apparatus were apparent to every fire chief. The horses were the biggest worry. In addition to their purchase and training costs, they generated ongoing expenses for horseshoes, fodder, hay, and veterinary care. Their stables and the space needed to store hay and grain took up a lot of room in the firehouse. Daily horse care—grooming, mucking out, exercising—took up a great deal of the firemen's time. The firemen on duty were in effect living above a stable, with all the attendant aroma, flies, and other drawbacks.

The steam engines were another worry. To start with, they were expensive. Extremely sturdy and efficient machines, they nonetheless required ongoing maintenance. Boiler explosions, though rare, did occur. Because steamers usually carried only enough fuel to operate for 30 minutes or so, tender wagons were needed to supply additional coal at working fires. The coal, the

tenders, and the horses needed to transport it all took up even more space in the firehouse. The noise, heat, cinders, and smoke generated by the steamers were unpleasant and messy for the firefighters, the horses, and the public.

Forward-looking fire chiefs everywhere saw clearly that the automobile could solve many of their problems. Less clear in the 1890s was what sort of automobile.

## ELECTRIC OR GASOLINE?

Electric fire vehicles were in use in Paris, Vienna, Hanover, and elsewhere in Europe by 1900. In Paris, an electric hose wagon, electric hook and ladder, and electric pumper were in routine use. Including the three-man crew and a 100-gallon water tank, the pumper weighed about 6,400 pounds. A primitive form of power take-off operated the pump. The motive power came from a battery of accumulators weighing some 1,300 pounds, suspended in a case below the vehicle. (The storage battery was perfected in France around 1880.) One charge allowed the vehicle to travel some 35 miles at an average speed of 12 miles an hour. In Vienna, an electric fire

engine capable of some 18 miles an hour (more than the speed limit in the city) was in use at the turn of the century.

In the United States, the first automobile ever used in the fire service was probably an electric runabout purchased in 1901 for the use of the chief engineer of the San Francisco fire department.

Lightweight, high-pressure steam engines were perfected in the period between 1860 and 1890, but it was the invention of the flash boiler in 1889 that made steam-powered automobiles really practical, since steam was raised almost instantly. In 1898, the identical twin brothers F.E. and F.O. Stanley began producing steam-powered autos. They quickly sold their design to the Locomobile Company, then almost immediately started another company to make Stanley Steamers. They soon encountered additional competition from the White Sewing Machine Company, which entered the steam automobile market in 1901.

The second automobile in the American fire service was most likely a steam-powered Locomobile purchased personally in 1901 by Chief Edward F. Croker of the Fire Department of New York. He donated it to the department and used it to travel to alarms.

At the dawn of the automotive age, steam vehicles had some significant advantages. They were relatively easy to make, since they had fewer moving parts; those parts did not require extremely exact machining to function well. Steamers were thus inexpensive; a Locomobile sold for about $600 in 1900. Steamers were based on a technology most drivers more or less understood; they couldn't stall; little gear-shifting was required. The best-selling American car in 1900 was the Locomobile.

As internal combustion engines became more reliable and powerful, however, the drawbacks of steamers became apparent. Steam engines were far less efficient than internal combustion engines of the same size and weight. They required frequent refills of water. They were no less expensive to operate, since the fuel for the boiler was gasoline.

Locomobile switched to internal combustion in 1903; White held out until 1910. Stanley Steamers were manufactured until 1925, but steam as a viable alternative to gasoline was effectively vanquished by 1905.

FIRE ENGINES

This combination wagon was built by White in 1914. Note the double bucket seats for the chauffeur and officer and the flared hose bed. The Springfield, Massachusetts, department supposedly invented the flared bed; the flaring allows crew benches along the hose bed.

At one time the electric automobile also seemed a good alternative to gas-powered cars. Electrics were silent, odorless, and easy to drive. No crank was needed to start them, and they had no gears to shift. In 1897, the Pope Manufacturing Company of Hartford, Connecticut, one of the country's leading bicycle manufacturers, began offering electric automobiles. A number of other manufacturers followed.

The electric automobile suffered the same fate as the steamer, but for somewhat different reasons. A primary problem was that electrics simply cost too much. The batteries had a range of only about 50 to 80 miles. (This was actually less of a problem than it sounds at a time when only about seven percent of all American roads were paved—car trips didn't usually cover that many miles.) Recharging the batteries required access to an electricity source at a time when, outside of large cities, electric power was rare. Recharging took a long time, and the storage batteries wore out quickly. The batteries were also extremely heavy compared to the size of the vehicle. Consequently, electrics were terrible when it came to hills.

Electric automobiles left the scene quickly. By 1907 Pope was out of business; Waverley was gone by 1915.

GASOLINE WINS OUT

By 1901 a few fire departments in Germany were using gasoline-powered automobile fire engines. The Magires four-man model had a two-cylinder, benzine-powered Daimler engine generating between 12 and 15 horsepower. The three-cylinder plunger pump threw 200 gallons a minute a distance of about 150 feet. An engineer riding a platform on the back of the vehicle operated the two-speed clutch, which gave speeds of 6 to 7½ miles per hour and 9 to 12 miles per hour, along with a slow reverse. Steering was usually done by a driver at the front, although the engineer could also steer from the back; both engineer and driver could operate independent brakes.

In the United States, automobiles were still seen as for chiefs only. In 1904, New York purchased two American Mercedes touring cars: one for the fire commissioner and one for the department chief. Chiefs elsewhere were giving up their horse-and-buggy outfits for automobiles. Other uses for automobiles were tried, including salvage wagons and squad cars.

It was not until 1906, however, that the first automobile fire engine went into service in the United States. The Radnor Fire Company of Wayne, Pennsylvania purchased a self-propelled, gasoline-powered motor pumping engine from the Waterous Engine Works of St. Paul, Minnesota. Waterous had been producing well-regarded steam pumpers utilizing duplex piston pumps since 1888. The orientation at Waterous was always toward pumps; the firm saw steam pumpers as simply another way to sell its pumping gear. To put pumps on a motorized chassis was simply a logical step forward.

The first Waterous rig had two separate motors. The rear-mounted pump could move 300 gallons a minute; a hose wagon accompanied the rig on all runs.

The second Waterous fire engine ever delivered was a 600-gpm machine purchased by the Alameda, California, department. Like the first Waterous, this rig was just a pumper; a hose tender went with it on all runs. Unlike the Radnor engine, however, the Alameda pumper had just one engine for both

propulsion and pumping. Important as the single-engine concept was for later motorized fire apparatus, it was less of a conceptual breakthrough than it appeared. Almost all self-propelled steamers used the same engine for propulsion and pumping, with the power take-off for pumping generally accomplished by jacking up the driving wheels; European motorized fire apparatus of the period generally used the same motor.

Successful as the Waterous motorized pumpers were (FDNY bought a gigantic pumper in 1912 and other departments bought a few pumpers up through 1919), the company eventually decided that pumps, not automobiles, were its business. Waterous remains today a leading supplier of pumping equipment.

In the first years the twentieth century, the reliability problems that

*The Springfield, Massachusetts fire department used this Knox electric combination wagon in the early part of the twentieth century; this photo was taken around 1914. The storage batteries are in the underslung compartment lettered S.F.D.*

*This little chemical and hose car was built on a 1915 Buick chassis.*

*Netco (New England Truck Company) assembled trucks from about 1914 through 1938 in Fitchburg, Massachusetts. The few hundred trucks Netco made were mostly sold locally. The Worcester, Massachusetts, fire department bought nine Netcos between 1916 and 1918 and outfitted them as fire trucks. The rig shown here, owned and restored by Jeff Trevas, is the only surviving Netco fire engine. It was originally designated Hose Wagon No. 7 as part of a two-piece engine company. Benches were fitted to the hose bed, however, making the vehicle more of a squad wagon. The original 4-cylinder engine was replaced by a 6-cylinder model in the early 1930s; the rig was retired by 1961.*

FIRE ENGINES

*America's first gasoline-powered ladder truck was built in 1909 by International Motor Company of New York City, the predecessor of Mack Trucks. The truck was sold to Allentown, Pennsylvania; Mack later moved all operations to Allentown. Here it poses with its ladder extended shortly after delivery.*

plagued early gasoline automobiles began to be resolved. For the fire service, the final impetus toward motorized apparatus was the great San Francisco earthquake of 1906. In its aftermath of destruction and fire, the acting fire chief of the city commandeered two hundred private automobiles for rescue operations. Even though the cars ended up running on their wheel rims because the heat and rough roads destroyed their tires, the chief later reported, "I was skeptical about the automobile previous to the disaster but now give it my hearty endorsement." And by February of 1909, the New York department had its first piece of motorized apparatus, a high-pressure hose wagon from the Knox Automobile Company in Springfield, Massachusetts. The wagon carried hose and a fixed turret nozzle, and was equipped with an acetylene searchlight. Top speed was 30 miles an hour.

Knox also built the first automobile chemical wagon in 1906. This vehicle offered two 35-gallon chemical tanks and achieved a top speed of 45 miles an hour.

## OLD FIRMS ENTER A NEW BUSINESS

That gasoline-powered apparatus was the future was clear to most of major manufacturers of fire apparatus. How to make the transition was far less clear. A period of consolidation was in store.

In 1891, a number of steam manufacturers, including Clapp & Jones, Button, and Silsby, merged with the Ahrens Manufacturing Company to form the American Fire Engine Company. The new firm manufactured steam pumpers based on an excellent design from the visionary Chris Ahrens, using the model names Metropolitan and Columbian.

The chief competition to the new company was the LaFrance Fire Engine Company, a relative upstart dating back only to 1872. LaFrance had quickly gained an outstanding reputation for excellent apparatus built with careful attention to the customer's needs.

The expected competitive advantages of consolidation never really materialized for the American Fire Engine Company. In 1901, another massive merger took place. The American Fire Engine Company combined with the LaFrance Fire Engine Company, the Amoskeag division of the Manchester Locomotive Works, and six smaller manufacturers to form a new company, the International Fire Engine Company. With all the operations firmly consolidated in the LaFrance plant at Elmira, New York, success was likely. The firm's name—though not its structure—was changed again in 1904 to American LaFrance Fire Engine Company.

American LaFrance moved into automotive fire engines in a tentative sort of way in 1907 with a chemical car later delivered to the Boston fire department. In 1909, the firm delivered two motorized combination chemical and hose wagons. It was not until 1910, however, that Lenox, Massachusetts, received the vehicle listed in the American LaFrance register as No. 1: a Type 5 combination hose and chemical car built on a four-cylinder Simplex chassis. More than twenty similar vehicles followed in that year alone. In 1911, American LaFrance began offering rotary-gear pumping engines in two sizes: Type 10 (500 gpm) and Type 12 (750 gpm). Savannah, Georgia, became the first completely motorized fire department in the country in 1911. The department was equipped entirely with American

The proud crew (plus a cigar-smoking sidewalk superintendent at the far right) poses with its new American LaFrance Type 5 chemical car around 1910. The location is unknown.

This American LaFrance Type 5 chemical car was delivered to Montgomery, Alabama, around 1910. Note the interesting large pneumatic tires on the rear wheels.

An American LaFrance Type 5 chemical car poses with all eleven members of the fire department in 1910. The location is unknown, but the photo was apparently taken by Theo LaFrance himself.

*The only remaining piece of Schnerr apparatus anywhere is this triple combination, built for San Francisco in 1915. The 500-gpm pump was inadequate, however, and San Francisco sold the rig to St. Helena, in the Napa Valley, in 1917. The engine is a 6-cylinder Wisconsin that could push the apparatus up to 50 mph; a 35-gallon chemical tank is also on board.*

LaFrance apparatus, including seven pumpers, four combination chemical and hose carts, and a straight chemical engine.

Even in 1912, the Fire Department of New York City wasn't wholly convinced that gasoline pumpers were the future. Just to be on the safe side, the department placed a large order for 28 American LaFrance second-size steamers. Drawn by Christie front-drive tractors, they ended up being the last steamers the department ever purchased. The FDNY order was not enough to convince ALF that a market for steamers still existed; the company produced its

*Aging apparatus tends to be cranky. Here the crew fills the radiator of an American LaFrance pumper from 1920. The occasion was the parade for FDNY's 125th anniversary in May, 1990.*

last steam pumper in 1914. (Interestingly, production of hand pumpers continued for several years after steamers were discontinued. The firm continued to repair steam pumpers into the 1920s.) The last steam pumper was delivered complete with the new American LaFrance Type 31 tractor to pull it.

ALF introduced the smaller Type 40 pumper in 1915 in 250-gpm and 350-gpm versions. A new model, the Type 14, was first sold in 1916. The Type 14 proved popular and was delivered in many configurations, including city service hook and ladder trucks and double combinations. In 1921, ALF

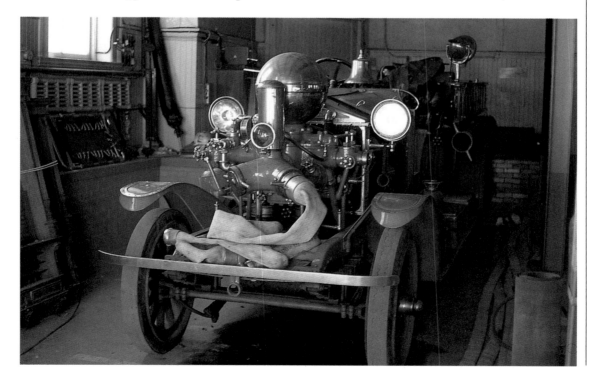

Ahrens-Fox model N-S-4 pumper, serial number 935, is still part of the roster at Alexandria Bay, New York. It was shipped in 1922.

offered the Type 14 as a quadruple combination with a full set of ladders, hose, volume pump, and a choice of booster or chemical equipment.

By 1917, American LaFrance had delivered FDNY's first substantial order of motorized fire apparatus: 25 of the new Type 75 700-gpm pumpers with rotary pumps. Fifteen more were delivered in 1919, 20 more in 1920, 20 more in 1921, and 28 more in 1922. With the deliveries in 1922, motorization of the department was complete.

From 1910 to 1917, American LaFrance made nearly 2,000 pieces of fire apparatus. This number exceeded the total production of all the other major manufacturers, including Seagrave and Ahrens-Fox, combined. Quality and dependability established American LaFrance as a leading manufacturer; volume kept purchase and maintenance costs reasonable.

Another established manufacturer able to make a successful transition to gasoline power was Seagrave. This firm had been making ladders, hook-and-ladder trucks, and chemical and hose combination wagons since 1881. In 1907, Seagrave produced its first motorized apparatus, a combination hose and chemical wagon given the model designation AC. Later that year, Seagrave made its first commercial delivery of motorized apparatus, sending two hose wagons and a straight chemical car to Vancouver. The Vancouver fire department became enthusiastic customers, purchasing a massive tractor-drawn aerial ladder and three smaller rigs in 1907. The air-cooled Seagrave model AC was also known as a "buckboard" because of its flat front and horse-wagon styling. While continuing to make buckboards, Seagrave introduced an engine-ahead design, the G model, in 1911. Its

first appearance was on Seagrave's first pumper, a 1,000 gpm rig sold to Oakland, California, in 1912. Power came from a massive 6-cylinder engine with a 9-inch stroke and 7½-inch bore, covered by a lengthy two-section hood. Mounted in the rear was a huge, three-stage Gorham centrifugal pump with 11-inch impellers. Seagrave sold about 40 similar pumpers, mostly to West Coast fire departments. By 1912 Seagrave was offering smaller apparatus using conventional centrifugal pumps ranging from 600 to 1,000 gpm.

An important innovation, the automatic pressure regulator, came from Seagrave in 1912. This device maintained a constant engine speed during pumping, providing a steady flow and helping to prevent engine overheating.

## AHRENS-FOX ENTERS THE MOTOR AGE

Chris Ahrens and the steam fire engine grew up together. As a young immigrant from Germany, Ahrens began working for Moses Latta, pioneer of steam self-propulsion, in 1856 at his Buckeye works in Cincinnati. After Buckeye merged with Lane & Bodley in 1863, Ahrens stayed on in the fire engine division. In 1868, Ahrens and a partner purchased the division and set up shop for themselves. Ahrens, a brilliant engineer, introduced his own excellent design in 1870. By 1875, the company had been renamed Ahrens Manufacturing Company.

After the 1891 merger that created the American Fire Engine Company, Ahrens hired a new engineer named Charles H. Fox. Among other innovations, Fox was responsible in 1893 for the design of the first steam-powered combination hose and pump fire engine. The first model was used to protect the

*A Knox piston pumper with an Amoskeag-type pump is at work for FDNY in this photo from around 1913. The buckboard style makes this rig resemble an early Seagrave.*

*Norwalk, Connecticut was served by this American LaFrance pumper. The chain drive is clearly visible on the rear tire. This photo was taken around 1910.*

*Leather bucket seats are a feature of this sleek-looking American LaFrance Type 5 chief's car. The photo was taken by Theo LaFrance at an unknown location in 1910.*

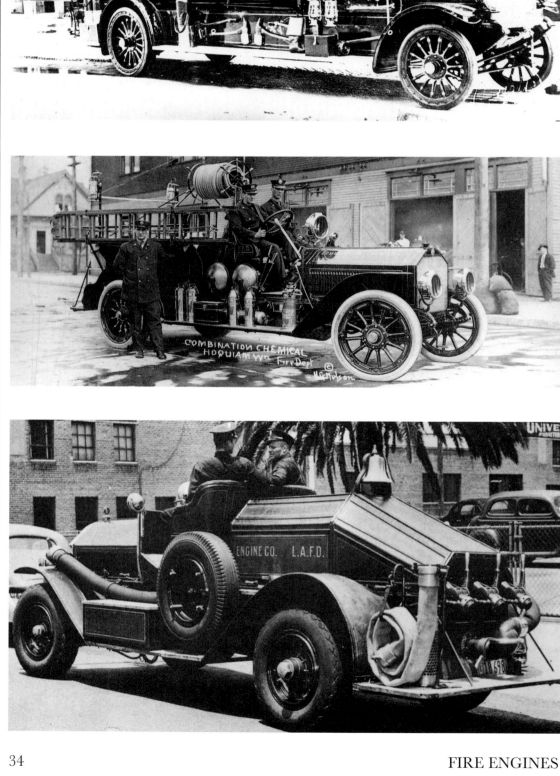

*One of the earliest Mack fire rigs is this city service hook and ladder truck, delivered to Morristown, New Jersey, in 1910.*

*This chemical combination wagon is an American LaFrance Type 75. It was delivered to Hoquiam, Washington, in the mid-1920s.*

*Seagrave delivered about forty of these massive pumpers equipped with 1,000-gpm Gorham Turbine pumps, mostly to West Coast departments, between 1911 and 1915. This rig, dating from 1913, served Los Angeles. A hose wagon accompanied it on runs; pumping operations took place in the rear. This photo was taken in the early 1940s, when pneumatic tires had replaced the original solid tires; the rig was scrapped in 1945.*

FIRE ENGINES

grounds of the Columbian Exposition which was then taking place in Chicago; the name Columbian was applied to the model thereafter.

In 1904, a year after the merger of American Fire Engine with the International Fire Engine Company, Chris Ahrens pulled his company out. A major patent dispute followed, but by 1905 Ahrens had reestablished himself as the Ahrens Fire Engine Company. Working at the factory in Cincinnati were Ahrens's sons George and John; Charles Fox was a vice president. In 1910, the firm changed its name again to Ahrens-Fox Fire Engine Company. Charles Fox was president and John Ahrens was vice president. Chris Ahrens had been inactive in company management since 1906; he died in 1919

Ahrens-Fox was surprisingly late in getting into motorized apparatus production. It was not until 1911 that the firm built its first motor pumper, dubbed the Model A. Assigned register number 500, this rig was consistently disappointing until the original pump was replaced with a 700-gpm twin-dome pump powered directly from the crankshaft. Renumbered 501, the new apparatus was placed in service at Rockford, Illinois, in January 1912. It proved itself almost immediately by pumping for 17 continuous hours in below-zero weather at a major fire.

Ahrens-Fox soon made up for lost time. At a competition for motorized apparatus held in New York City in 1913, a Model A won easy honors, pumping nonstop for 12 hours. None of the other rigs, including apparatus from American LaFrance, Nott, Knox, and other manufacturers, came close to the Model A's reliability and efficiency. In 12 hours, the rig used 117 gallons of gas and managed a top rate of 746 gpm at a pressure of 135 pounds per square inch.

The famed Ahrens-Fox piston pump, with its shiny spherical air chamber, was introduced in 1914 as standard equipment on the Model K pumpers; Charles Fox received the patent in 1916. Ahrens-Fox also purchased the patent rights to the Mooers motor. Thus the most critical parts of all Ahrens-Fox fire engines were of outstanding quality and proprietary design. The result was apparatus that was powerful, durable, reliable—and expensive. The model MK2 750-gpm pumpers purchased by New York City in 1915 cost over $7,000 each.

One of the most popular Ahrens-Fox designs was the Model N, a powerful 1,000-gpm pumper that stayed in production, with several major modifications, from 1917 until 1935. Other models introduced in the teens and early twenties included the J, K, L, M, M-K, and P. It was an M-K that made fire apparatus and publicity history in July 1917 by pumping a stream 796 feet over the Woolworth Building in New York City. The Model J, introduced in 1919, was a six-cylinder model with shaft drive, a stylishly gabled hood, and a 750-gpm pump. This model remained in production for 11 more years.

In 1913, Charles H. Fox had yet another inspired idea, one that again changed the face of firefighting. He mounted a small gasoline-powered centrifugal pump in front of the radiator of a light-duty commercial truck chassis. The pump was fed by an auxiliary water tank located behind the driver's seat. The system quickly became known as the booster tank, and it rapidly displaced the function of the chemical wagon. Booster tanks were also quickly incorporated into pumpers, thus producing one of the most durable and effective concepts in modern firefighting: the triple combination fire engine, featuring a booster pump, volume pump, and hose. The Cincinnati fire department was the first to take delivery of Ahrens-Fox rigs with booster tanks.

An amazing number of Ahrens-Fox rigs remained in active and reserve service for decades. Of the 285 Model N rigs, for example, over 130 are still in existence. Lovingly preserved, many Ahrens-Fox fire engines are still seen today in museums and as parade pieces.

## NEW FIRMS BEGIN

In 1899, some thirty American manufacturers produced about 2,500 motorized vehicles. By 1907, production had reached 44,000 automobiles a year. Between 1900 and 1908, nearly 500 companies were or had been in the automobile business in the United States; by 1908, about 250 were still active. By 1913, annual American production of motor vehicles was about 485,000 units out of a worldwide total of about 606,000.

At the beginning of the automobile age, entry into the marketplace was relatively easy. The components needed to assemble a motor vehicle were easily obtained from outside sources; the skills required to put the pieces together were not that different from the skills workers already had. The capital required was relatively small. Henry Ford began the Ford Motor Company in 1901 with a paid-in capital of just $28,000, a handful of workers, and a tiny assembly area. His chassis, including the axles, motor, and transmission, came from the Dodge brothers.

Given the ease of entry, it is not surprising that a number of companies in seemingly unrelated businesses got into the automotive line and, by extension, into fire trucks. The Tea Tray Manufac-

turing Company of Newark, New Jersey, is often cited as an incongruous example. This company is credited with making the first triple combination truck (hose, pump, and chemical tank), which went into service with the Monhagen Hose Company of Middletown, New York, in 1909. The rig was built on an American Mors automobile chassis and equipped with a commercially built 400-gpm pump. Since the only original work on the fire engine was the metal fabrication and stamping for the body work—an area where the Tea Tray Company presumably had expertise—on closer examination the company was actually on to a good thing. Of course, Tea Tray and many other would-be motor moguls such as the Davis Sewing Machine Company never really got off the ground, producing at most a few forgotten rigs.

Many small or struggling manufacturers were put out of business by 1908, the year Henry Ford began offering the Model T and William Durant founded General Motors. A wave of consolidation and rationalization of the automotive industry followed—a difficult process that has been repeated at intervals ever since.

The Model T brought true acceptance of the automobile to the American public. Sturdy, lightweight, with a high clearance for rutted dirt road, it was ideal for getting around in rural America. It was also inexpensive. A 1907 Model T cost $850; by 1927, the last year of Model T production, the car cost only $290. Any shade-tree mechanic could easily mount a small pump, chemical tank, and other lightweight firefighting apparatus on a Model T. When the Ford Model TT truck was introduced in 1917, it proved extremely popular with small, rural fire depart-

McKeesport, Pennsylvania, was the home of this American LaFrance Type 38 combination rig. In 1919, left-hand drive was still not standard.

This gasoline-propelled second-size Nott steamer was built as a single unit (not tractorized) for FDNY in 1911 as one of the department's earliest pieces of motorized apparatus. Part of the complex chain drive and differential system is visible by the rear wheel. This rig served with Engine Company 58, but proved unsatisfactory and was taken out of service within a year.

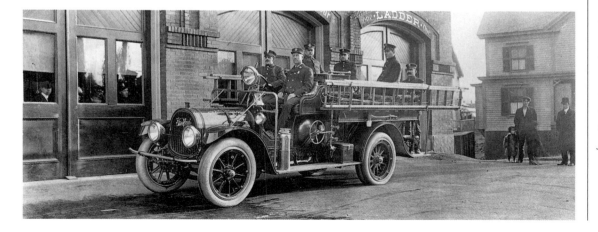

Pope-Hartford started as a bicycle manufacturer and switched to automobiles in 1897. This combination chemical car served South Framingham, Massachusetts. The picture dates from around 1910.

ments. The basic chassis was locally adapted in countless ways to provide inexpensive fire protection. Major manufacturers such as American LaFrance also offered inexpensive fire apparatus (usually small chemical cars) built on Model T chassis.

Numerous other established truck and auto manufacturers extended their lines to fire apparatus, some more successfully than others. Commercial chassis from virtually every manufacturer were modified for fire apparatus at some point. Old registers from before 1914 or so record rigs built on chassis from Kissel, Autocar, Pope-Hartford, and even Cadillac.

At the start of World War I, orders for light trucks went mostly to the makers of large, heavy chassis for luxury cars such as Packard and Peerless. By the end of the war, however, Nash Motor Company emerged as a leader in truck manufacturing. The lesson was clear to automobile manufacturers: Trucks (including fire apparatus) were no longer just bigger cars. Many small or inflexible manufacturers stuck chiefly to passenger cars or went under altogether at the war's end. Better-established manufacturers such as Maxim, Nott, Knox, White, Robinson, Stutz, Boyd, Webb, and many others stayed in the business and produced interesting, sometimes innovative fire apparatus in the period up to the late 1920s.

Apparatus from Nott, for example, was used in the earliest years of the FDNY's motorization program. A particularly interesting transitional rig was a gasoline-propelled steam pumper delivered in 1911. Innovative but ineffective, this rig stayed in service for less than a year. Two conventional Nott pumpers delivered in 1913 were more successful.

One company that made a very successful entry into the fire apparatus market was Peter Pirsch & Sons of Kenosha, Wisconsin. Pirsch had a significant advantage over other newcomers, however, since the firm was already a well-regarded supplier of ladders and chemical apparatus. Pirsch had been building chemical cars and ladder wagons for years. The first Pirsch pumper, a triple combination built on a White Motor Company truck chassis, didn't arrive until 1916. The 500-gpm rig with a Rumsey pump went to Creston, Iowa. Pirsch used a variety of chassis for fire apparatus in the teens and twenties, including Duplex, White, and Ford Model TT.

THE MACK BROTHERS ARRIVE
The five Mack brothers began building horse wagons in 1889 in Brooklyn. In 1901, brother Jack was taken for his first automobile ride. The driver mentioned to Jack that a gasoline motor could easily be used to propel a truck or bus. This casual remark had awesome results. The Mack Brothers Company built its first bus in the winter of 1902-03, and a second in 1904. The company began producing its own engines in 1904.

Although Mack moved to Pennsylvania in 1904 and began commercial truck production at the new factory in Allentown in 1905, the firm did not enter the fire apparatus business until 1910. What is probably the first motorized city service hook and ladder truck in America was delivered by Mack to Morristown, New Jersey, in 1910. The first real Mack fire engine consisted of a pump mounted on a Senior Series heavy-duty truck chassis. This rig went to the Union Fire Association of Lower Merion, a suburb of Philadelphia, in 1911. By 1912 Mack was delivering apparatus to New York City, which

A Schacht hose wagon and a Schacht four-wheel tractor are shown in this photo from around 1916. The apparatus belonged to Newport, Kentucky.

This small chemical wagon was built by Howe on an Acme chassis in 1916 for the Cadillac, Michigan, fire department.

Mack Trucks began selling fire engines in 1919 using the AC chassis. This combination rig, shown ready to draft from a culvert around 1920, has a 500-gpm rotary-gear pump.

became a steady customer for the next sixty years and more. The first Mack delivery to FDNY was three buckboard-type high-pressure hose wagons; three others with Mack chassis but bodywork by Boyd were also delivered that year. In addition, 21 Mack/Boyd engine-ahead combination chemical wagons, called Scouts, were also delivered.

The small AB chassis was introduced in 1914. The instantly recognizable four-cylinder AC chassis, with its famed sloping nose and stylized M on the grille, was introduced in 1915. The durability of this model gave rise to the expression "built like a Mack truck." The AC chassis remained in production until 1927.

## THE LAST OF THE HORSES

As motorization took over the fire houses of America, many a tearful ceremony was held to retire the beloved fire horses. By the start of the 1920s, such ceremonies were becoming rarer. One of the most belated was the last regular run of the FDNY fire horses, which took place at a special ceremony at Brooklyn's Borough Hall on 20 December 1922.

The retirement ceremonies were the symbolic end of a firefighting era. In the larger picture, however, the age of the horse ended definitively in 1921 with the passage of the Federal Highway Act. The law provided matching federal grants to the states for the construction of an interstate highway system. By 1922, more than 10,000 miles of federally financed roads had been built. The automobile had triumphed.

*The last run of the fire horses in New York City took place on December 20, 1922. Engine Company 205 in Brooklyn Heights was special-called to Borough Hall, where, with appropriate ceremony, the horses were replaced by a new American LaFrance pumper.*

# Chapter Three

# Tractors, Towers, and Trolleys

Expensive and built to last, the steam engines that filled most fire houses at the turn of the century were annoyingly slow to wear out and justify their replacement with shiny new automotive rigs. Heavy-duty aerial ladders and water towers also represented large investments in perfectly functional equipment. An ingenious solution that kept the apparatus while replacing the horses was to attach tractors to the rigs.

## TRACTORIZATION

Several manufacturers had begun to supply tractors to the fire service by around 1910. The Couple Gear Freight Wheel Company pioneered by offering an electric drive system. The motive power to each wheel of the four-wheel tractor was provided by an individual electric motor powered by batteries. The big problem was that the batteries tended to run out of power on the way back from the fire. The apparatus would then have to be towed ignominiously back to the fire house. Couple Gear later replaced the batteries with a gasoline-powered electric generator mounted under the frame. Springfield, Massachusetts, purchased a Couple Gear tractor in 1910 to pull an 85-foot Seagrave

aerial ladder. In 1912, New York purchased four Couple Gear electric ladder trucks. Ahrens-Fox experimented briefly with Couple Gear tractors in 1912, producing just a few tractors designed to pull steam engines. Couple Gear had some success providing electric-drive chassis for fire apparatus, but by 1920 the firm was no longer in business.

A more functional, four-cylinder, internal combustion tractor was developed by a true automotive pioneer and racing champion, John Walter Christie. His two-wheel, transverse-engine design was sturdy, simple, and powerful. Production began at Christie's Front Drive Auto Company plant in Hoboken, New Jersey, in 1912. A major order for 28 tractors came almost immediately from New York City. By 1917, 153 Christie tractors were in service; FDNY would eventually have some 300 Christie tractors, about half of the total production. These tough tractors could pull up to 12 tons.

After 1919, J. Walter Christie stopped producing tractors and directed his talents toward tank design. A major problem with the tracked suspension of early tanks was that they tended to break down while trundling to the battlefield.

*An American LaFrance Type 31 tractor was used to replace the horses on this steamer, shown in operation at a muster. The homemade windshield was a later addition*

*This 1916 American LaFrance Type 31 tractor tows a 1906 American LaFrance steam engine.*

FIRE ENGINES

Christie first proposed a tank that ran on wheels until it reached the fighting, at which point attached bogies were lowered (raising the driving wheels off the ground) and treads attached. His early models were tested and rejected by the Ordnance Department. Christie then turned his efforts to lightweight, high-speed tank chassis. In 1922, Christie reorganized the Front Drive Motor Company as the U.S. Wheel Track Layer Corporation and moved to Rahway, New Jersey. His new tank designs won approval from the military, and Christie spent the next ten years or so building prototypes and a limited number of tanks. By 1932, disputes with the military over Christie's T3 medium tank design ended the relationship. Interestingly, however, Christie sold two of these tanks to the Soviet Union. These became the model for the famous T34

Soviet tank, which was instrumental in the defeat of the Nazis on the eastern front in World War II.

C.J. Cross, a former employee of J. Walter Christie, set up his own firm to manufacture tractors in 1914. The engine in Cross tractors was conventionally mounted parallel to the frame.

American LaFrance began producing tractors with the Type 17 around 1912 and the Type 31 in 1913. The Type 17 was a four-wheel tractor that had a 6-cylinder, 105 horsepower engine with double side-chain drive; the bore was 5½ inches and the stroke was 6 inches. The transmission allowed three forward speeds and one reverse. The Type 17 was designed for aerial trucks, but it was never as popular for that purpose as the Type 31. The two-wheeled Type 31 for aerial trucks had a vertically mounted steering wheel. It was available in two versions: a 4-cylinder,

75-horsepower engine or a 6-cylinder, 105-horsepower engine. Both versions used double side chains. The wheels were cast steel, solid-disc type. The Type 31 tractor for steamers offered a 4-cylinder, 75-horsepower engine with double side-chain drive. The Type 31 remained in production until 1929, pulling steamers, aerial ladders, and water towers.

Seagrave delivered a tractor-drawn aerial ladder to Vancouver in 1909; the motive power came from a four-wheel Model AC-90 with a 4-cylinder, air-cooled engine. Seagrave offered the 6-cylinder Model K tractor starting in 1915. It never achieved the popularity of the Type 31. In the twenties, Seagrave offered the model W-656, which was used by a number of departments to motorize water towers. A few smaller apparatus makers offered tractors in the teens and twenties, including Garford, Boyd, Knox, and Robinson.

Knox-Martin of Springfield, Massachusetts began offering a peculiar three-wheeled tractor around 1909. The steering column extended over the hood to the single front wheel. The advantage of the single wheel was that it could turn nearly 90 degrees, thus allowing greater maneuverability for large, clumsy apparatus such as aerial ladders. Powered by a 40-horsepower, 4-cylinder engine, these tractors could get up to 30 miles per hour. In a burst of civic pride, Springfield used a Knox-Martin to motorize its 1894 65-foot Champion water tower in 1911. Knox-Martins achieved a certain level of popularity, but they were never real competition for American LaFrance or Seagrave.

As the old steam pumps wore out or were finally replaced in the 1920s and early 1930s, the demand for tractors lessened sharply and companies such as Cross stopped making them. Many aerial ladders and water towers, however, stayed in service so long that their original tractors needed replacement.

## AERIAL LADDERS

Although an astonishing number of idiotic ideas for aerial ladders were patented in the latter half of the 1800s, a few concepts were worthwhile and entered production.

The first truly successful aerial ladder was designed by Daniel D. Hayes, the chief mechanic of the San Francisco Fire

Department. In 1868, Hayes patented a design for an 85-foot wooden aerial ladder mounted on a turntable. The ladder was raised by using a single horizontal worm gear. A large nut on the turntable was attached to braces that were in turn attached to the butt end of the ladder. Revolving the worm gear moved the nut forward and raised the ladder. Conceptually sound, the first Hayes aerials had a few drawbacks. The horses had to be unhitched before the four to six burly firefighters needed to turn the elevating handle could get to it. In addition, the tillerman rode in a compartment under the ladder, which restricted his view considerably. Nonetheless, a few aerials based on the original design were sold. San Francisco took the prototype around 1872, paying $3,000.

Hayes's ladder was a bit of a sensation in its time, since ladders prior to his invention were limited to 50 to 60 feet in length. In 1883, Hayes sold his patents to the LaFrance Fire Engine Company. By 1886, two LaFrance Hayes 85-foot aerials had been delivered to New York City. The model proved popular and soon a number of departments had LaFrance Hayes aerials.

A competing design was offered by the Fire Extinguisher Manufacturing Company. E. Steck, a foreman there, patented an aerial ladder design in 1884. The first aerial built to this design became known as the Babcock and was demonstrated in 1886. Raising the Babcock was accomplished by means of vertical worm screws on either side of the ladder's base; each worm screw was connected to a hand crank by bevel gearing. Two firemen could thus raise the Babcock quickly by turning the hand cranks. Babcocks achieved moderate success. The first was bought by New Haven in 1887; within the next two years, 24 Babcocks were in service in various cities.

Another successful aerial design came from Gleason & Bailey of Seneca Falls, New York. In 1895, the firm introduced the 85-foot Dederick Aerial Ladder. The raising mechanism for the Dederick consisted of raising arms connected to bronze cables, which were in turn connected through pulleys to a drum at the base of the ladder. The drum was revolved using crank handles attached to a chain-link reduction drive. Dederick aerials could be raised quickly and easily. FDNY purchased an 85-foot Dederick in 1896. In 1900, Gleason & Bailey became part of American LaFrance; the Dederick aerial was offered by American LaFrance for several years after the merger.

A major step forward in aerial ladder design came in the late 1880s, when Chief E.F. Dahill of New Bedford, Massachusetts, invented a system for raising aerial ladders using pistons

*A beautifully preserved 1914 Knox-Martin three-wheeled tractor pulls an 1898 American LaFrance steam engine in San Jose, California. The long steering column connects to a gearbox above the single front wheel. This is one of only two Knox-Martin tractors known to still exist; the other is in the Smithsonian Institution.*

powered by compressed air. The Dahill Air Hoist, as it was called, was soon offered by most aerial manufacturers. In 1902 Seagrave offered a patented spring-operated hoist system to raise the aerial. Twin lifting springs raised the main part of the ladder; cranks and a worm screw extended it. This system, which came to be called "manual spring-assist," had a major impact on the aerial business. American LaFrance introduced a spring-assist aerial in 1904. The complex mechanism featured a hydraulic cylinder to control the extension of the ladder—the first step toward the all-hydraulic systems that would later predominate. Other manufacturers offering spring-assist raising included Pirsch and Ahrens-Fox. Later improvements led to combinations of spring and compressed air, eliminating the hand-cranked worm screw entirely. By the 1930s, when the modified older aerials drawn by tractors had been replaced by newer models, aerials were lifted hydraulically, using a power take-off from the transmission.

By the turn of the century, most cities had some aerial ladders and were adding more. In 1900, for instance, FDNY received five 85-foot aerials: four Dedericks from Gleason & Bailey and one Hayes LaFrance. A 70-foot Babcock was also received that year.

A typical aerial ladder with a crew of eight weighed around 12,000 pounds. A team of three well-trained, strong horses was needed to haul it. In terms of logistics, this presented a real problem. Even the strongest horses tired after about half a mile at top speed. Aerial ladders responding to multiple alarm fires were therefore very slow to arrive. The solution was motorization.

Among the earliest motorized aerial ladders were four delivered to New York City in 1912 by the Webb Motor Fire Apparatus Company of St. Louis. Powered by Couple Gear electric drive tractors, these rigs were extremely slow and were soon placed in reserve. By 1913, FDNY was using Christie tractors to pull some aerials and had also purchased motorized Type 18 aerials from American LaFrance. By 1917, American LaFrance was soon offering the popular Type 17 and Type 31 models as tillered aerial trucks in 4-cylinder, 75-horse-power and 6-cylinder, 105-horsepower versions. The choice of ladders ranged from 55 to 85 feet. Seagrave was in the aerial business with the Model K and later Model L, and Mack was offering the Model AC-7.

## WATER TOWERS

As buildings grew taller and cities grew denser in the 1880s, the need for a way to pour a powerful stream of water into the upper stories of a burning building became acute. The solution was what came to be known as the water tower.

The first true water tower was invented in 1876 by Albert and Abner Greenleaf and John B. Logan, all of Baltimore. The name aptly given by the partners to their invention was "Portable Stand-Pipe or Water Tower." The Greenleaf water tower, as it came to be known, consisted of three sections. A base pipe was permanently mounted on the floor of a horse-drawn wagon; a straight pipe or mast was attached to the base; and a 1H-inch diameter extension mast pipe with a built-in nozzle tip was attached to the straight pipe. The assem-

blage was raised by hand cranking an arrangement of gears on a trunnion. A hand-cranked wheel at the rear operated the leveling system, while a cable braced the main mast against back pressure.

A 50-foot Greenleaf water tower was successfully demonstrated in June of 1879, and was loaned to the New York Fire Department in July of that year. In

*The American LaFrance Type 31 4-cylinder tractor for aerial trucks was extremely popular. The tractor used cast steel solid disk wheels with dual solid tires. It generated 75 horsepower.*

*The American LaFrance Type 31 6-cylinder tractor for aerial trucks was designed for heavier ladders; it generated 105 horsepower.*

*Aerial trucks from American LaFrance were sold with the Type 31 6-cylinder tractor. Ladders were offered in a choice of 55, 65, 75, or 85 feet; additional ground ladders were standard equipment. The ladder trailer came with artillery-style wheels.*

1881, New York purchased the loaner for $4,000. Greenleaf delivered a second 50-foot water tower to FDNY in 1882. This tower had a 2½-inch extension mast pipe and interchangeable nozzle tips. Although this tower overturned during acceptance tests, it was nonetheless accepted for service with some modification to the counterweight system of bracing. One more Greenleaf, a 50-foot tower for Boston, was delivered in 1882. In 1883, the Greenleaf patent was sold to the Fire Extinguisher Manufacturing Company (FEMCO). Only one more water tower was built on the Greenleaf patent, however, because the design quickly became obsolete.

In 1886, George C. Hale, chief of the Kansas City, Missouri, fire department, patented a manually raised water tower. Hale's real breakthrough came a few years later, in 1889, when he invented a combination chemical-hydraulic lifting system for his water tower. Water pressure was used to force a soda-acid mixture from the chemical tank into two lifting cylinders. The carbon dioxide produced in the cylinders moved pistons that engaged a gear assembly and raised the tower to an upright position. Hale built twenty towers on this model; the chemical tanks and cylinders came from FEMCO. From 1886 to 1892, Hale produced almost all the water towers made, delivering 38 in all.

FEMCO eventually gave up on the Greenleaf design and challenged Hale with an entirely new approach to water towers. The new Champion model utilized the excellent Greenleaf nozzle and was placed on a turntable instead of on trunnions. This meant that the tower could operate at an angle out of vertical, providing vastly increased flexibility.

Champion water towers were raised by hand. Two men were needed on either side of the mast to turn handles connected to bevel gears. The nozzle pipe was extended using a hand crank connected to gears that moved a cable.

*FDNY Ladder Company No. 146 motors along in Williamsburg with its 75-foot American LaFrance aerial ladder in 1913.*

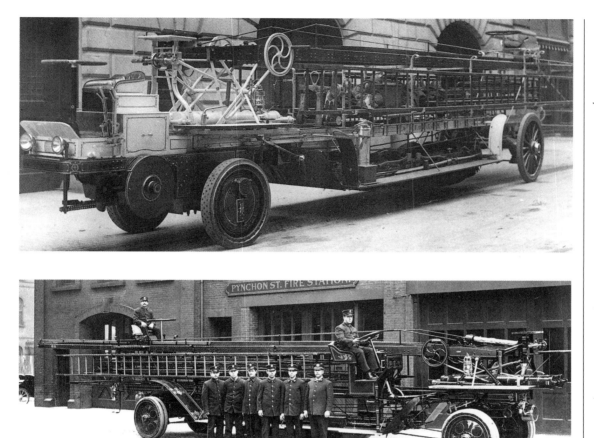

The six early Champion towers had the turntable in the front and the nozzle hanging over the rear. In the 15 later versions built after 1894, the design was reversed.

Sales of the Champion tower were so strong that in 1894 George Hale sold his patents to FEMCO and retired. FEMCO thus had a near monopoly on water tower sales.

In 1898, a new water tower design attracted wide attention. Henry H. Gorter, a fire department mechanic in San Francisco, came up with the idea of using a water pump motor as the raising mechanism, eliminating slow and tiring hand cranking. In addition, the tower could be raised or lowered while in operation. It could also operate at an angle of 35 degrees in either direction from perpendicular and could be swung through the angles while in operation. When the mast was swung through its entire oscillation of 70 degrees, it covered a frontage of 90 feet.

Gorter's design also featured a nozzle that connected to the supply pipe via a ball-and-socket joint. This allowed the nozzle to rotate 360 degrees in the horizontal and almost 180 degrees in the vertical. The full extension of the tower was 76 feet, making it the highest water tower ever built. The tower received its water from eight 3-inch inlets sur-

mounted by an air chamber to minimize excessive pumping vibration. To work at maximum capacity, the Gorter tower needed to receive water from four first-class steam pumpers; maximum output was 4,500 gpm. The total weight of the tower was about 1,500 pounds. Three horses were needed to pull it.

Excellent as the Gorter tower was, only four were initially produced: two for San Francisco and two for Los Angeles. In 1926, the San Francisco department dusted off the old plans and produced two more 350-foot Gorter water towers, pulled by Mack AC tractors. These two unusual rigs are now parade pieces in San Francisco.

As part of the big merger of 1900, FEMCO became part of the International Fire Engine Company. In this incarnation, a 65-foot FEMCO-design water tower was delivered to New York City in 1904. That same year, International Fire Engine Company was incorporated into American LaFrance. In effect, this meant that American LaFrance now had the near-monopoly on water towers. The first water tower from the new management was a 55-footer delivered to Atlanta in 1904. New York got its first American LaFrance tower, 65-foot, hydraulic-raise model, in 1910.

The only real competition left in the water tower area came from Seagrave, which had introduced a new spring-raise mechanism. The first two versions of the new design were constructed at the Seagrave factory in Canada and went to Winnipeg in 1905 and Montreal in 1906. The first American-built Seagrave water tower went to New York City in 1907. Sixty-five feet long, it was placed in service with a three-horse hitch.

The first motorized water tower was FDNY's 1904 65-foot International Fire Company. This unit received a Webb-Couple gasoline/electric tractor in 1912. The unit ended up being extremely heavy, weighing more than 10 tons. The first tractor lasted until 1923, when it was replaced with a four-wheel Mack AC Bulldog. In 1930, the tower received its third tractor, a four-wheel Walter. After a period as a reserve unit, the tower received its fourth tractor, a 1953 six-wheel Ward LaFrance. The tower was finally junked in 1957.

The first water tower to be delivered motorized was an American Automatic 65-footer from American LaFrance. It was delivered with a two-wheel Type 30 tractor to New Orleans in 1914. The first FDNY water tower to be bought already motorized was a 1923 FEMCO/American LaFrance 65-foot model. It was propelled by a Type 17 tractor. The cost was a mere $18,000. The 65-foot Seagrave water tower put into FDNY service in 1929 cost $21,000. This tower raised hydraulically at a pressure of 80 pounds in about 30 seconds.

Tractorization kept many water towers in service for decades. A number of water towers weren't officially junked or retired until after 1940; a few have ended up in museums or private hands. Ahrens-Fox, Christie, Mack, Seagrave, and American LaFrance tractors, along with a few lesser-known names, were all used to motorize these massive rigs. The towers themselves were frequently wrecked. Survivors were often modified and rebuilt, necessary because they had an unfortunate way of toppling over due to back pressure. The days of the water tower were numbered, however. Starting in the 1930s, they were superseded by more effective steel aerials that combined the water-delivery ability of the tower with the rescue capability of a ladder. Seagrave, for example, by 1935

*A 1923 tractorized Seagrave aerial ladder awaits restoration. This 85-foot ladder served Syracuse, New York, for many years.*

had developed a service aerial ladder truck with a 65-foot all-steel ladder in three sections; the ladder was hydraulically raised.

The last commercial water tower was an American Automatic from American LaFrance. Delivered to Los Angeles in 1938, this 65-foot, spring-raised rig was drawn by a Series 400 tractor.

## FIRE-FIGHTING TROLLEYS

In the 1890s, interurban electric traction railways—better known as trolleys—were being built at a very rapid pace in Europe and North America. An extensive interconnected network of overhead electric lines soon crisscrossed cities and even small towns. By transferring frequently, it was possible by 1900 to travel by trolley from Boston to New York.

Creative minds seized on the trolley as a way to get firefighting equipment to a conflagration quickly. In 1897, the Wason Manufacturing Company of Springfield, Massachusetts, devised an electric engine truck. In effect, the apparatus consisted of two four-wheel bogies attached to either end of platform. To load the steam pumper onto the platform, the front bogie was disconnected and run ahead; the steamer was winched onto the platform; finally, the front bogie was backed up and reconnected. Firefighters, hose, tools and other equipment rode on platforms on the bogies. At a test of the system, the steamer was loaded in 2¼ minutes. It was unloaded in 45 seconds; the horses were harnessed and ready to go 1¼ minutes after that. The firefighters presumably ran after the horses, carrying their gear.

Another ingenious trolley idea that never really caught on was horse-drawn, electrically powered pumps taking their power from the overhead trolley wires that crisscrossed urban and suburban areas by 1900. Conceptually, this was not all that different from the horse-drawn, gasoline-powered pumps that were in use here and there by the early

*FDNY Water Tower No. 1, a hydraulically raised FEMCO 65-footer from 1898, rushes to the blaze. This became the first water tower to be motorized when a Webb-Couple Gear tractor was attached in 1911. Weighing over ten tons, this water tower was also the heaviest piece of equipment of its period. The tower was junked in the 1970s.*

1900s. An experimental electric model with an eight-horsepower, direct-current motor was tried out by the Paris Fire Department in 1903. The centrifugal pump was carried on a two-wheeled, one-horse cart; a "jumper" hose reel with 660 feet of hose was attached to the cart. A reel of wire also 660 feet long was mounted on the cart, allowing a theoretical range of 1,320 feet for the stream. The total weight of the apparatus, including the two-man crew, was 2, 288 pounds, quite light when compared to a typical LaFrance steamer of the time, which weighed nearly 10,000 pounds. The electric pump could pump only 77 gallons per minute.

The French electric cart doesn't seem to have crossed the Atlantic, but some firefighters in America were thinking along similar lines. Captain John Fenlon of FDNY Engine 72 suggested in 1903 that municipalities specify, when granting contracts for trolley lines and electric lights, that leads be run from overhead electric lines down to every fire hydrant on the route. The battery-

powered fire engines that were definitely the wave of the future could then be used; the electric pumps would simply be plugged into the outlets.

One firefighting trolley that did work was found in Duluth, Minnesota from 1907 to 1930. The trolley provided fire protection to the residents of Park Point, a long, narrow strip of land extending across Lake Superior. Only four to six hundred feet in width, the suburb (at that time mostly summer houses) was connected to the mainland by a bridge; a single street with a trolley line ran the length of the settled portion of the strip.

The trolley was a modified regular car with the seats removed and a hose box installed along its whole length; the cost was $650. The equipment consisted of 1,500 feet of 2½-inch hose, a 35-gallon chemical tank, 200 feet of ¾-inch chemical hose, numerous ground and roof ladders, axes, pike poles, two six-gallon Babcock extinguishers, and rubber hats and coats for the volunteers. Under an agreement with the trolley company, the car was stored in a spe-

The raising mechanism of FDNY's 1907 65-foot Seagrave water tower can be seen very clearly in this shot. The firefighter on the right is turning the handwheel that extends the inner mast pipe; the firefighter in the center is maneuvering the mast nozzle by using a hand crank. The white horizontal cylinders contain the raising springs. The tractor is a 1914 Garford; the picture was taken around 1920.

One of the last water towers ever built was this 65-foot spring-raised American Automatic, purchased by Newark, New Jersey, in 1936. The 6-wheel tractor is an American LaFrance 400 Series Metropolitan. The duplex mast had a high-pressure nozzle at the top and another halfway up. Two deck guns were on the trailer platform. The upper nozzle and the deck guns were supplied by 12 intakes through 6-inch manifolds; the lower mast nozzle had its own three intakes. Four to five pumpers were needed to supply the tower. The tower saw little actual service and was scrapped in 1958.

cially built house; for a fee of $30 a month, the company kept the trolley in good repair and furnished a motorman to drive it. When an alarm was turned in, the trolley was started down the tracks and picked up volunteers along the way.

*Water Tower No. 1 was in active service in Syracuse, New York, from 1923 to 1964. After some years in reserve and additional years as a parade piece, the tower was sold to a private collector in 1978. The tower is a 65-foot American Automatic. The original American LaFrance Type 31 two-wheel tractor wore out and was replaced in 1957 with a 1927 Seagrave tractor scavenged from another Syracuse water tower that was scrapped.*

*The Duluth, Minnesota, fire trolley ran from 1907 to 1930. In this photo from the 1920s, the ever-vigilant firemen pose in their turnout gear on the trolley car. Ladders hang on the sides; an electric pump, hose, and other equipment are stored inside the car.*

FIRE ENGINES

*Chapter Four*

# New Developments in Apparatus

With the last horses retired and the internal combustion engine firmly established in the fire house, the inevitable next step was the improvement of motorized fire apparatus. The field was open to innovation in the period from the 1920s to just after World War II.

## POSTWAR PROSPERITY

Peacetime prosperity after 1918 brought an amazing surge in the purchase of automobiles. In 1916, some 3.4 million cars were registered in the United States. By 1930, the number was 23.1 million. Less spectacularly but still indicative of municipal growth, American LaFrance had sold over 4,000 fire engines in the period from 1910 to 1926.

## AMERICAN LAFRANCE DOMINATES

As the 1920s began, American LaFrance was well established as the predominant producer of fire apparatus. Several highly successful models such as the Type 17 and Type 31 were in widespread use in a variety of configurations.

In the early 1920s, American LaFrance introduced several new models. The very popular Type 75 750-gpm triple-combination pumper came in

1922, powered by a 6-cylinder, 105-horsepower American LaFrance engine. The smaller Type 40, with a 350-gpm pump and a four-cylinder, 75-horsepower engine, was first sold in 1923. The Type 14 city service hook and ladder truck remained popular, as were the Type 17 aerial and Type 31 front-drive aerial or water tower. The light-duty Cosmopolitan model, built on a commercial Brockway chassis, was also first offered in 1923.

A new range of fire apparatus, the 100 Series, was introduced in 1926 and continued until 1931. The biggest changes were a completely new radiator design and two rows of louvers on the hood. Perhaps the best-known rigs in this series were the Type 145 Metropolitans. This version had a 6-cylinder engine and carried a 1,000 gpm rotary gear pump.

The Master Series rigs (Type 200) began in 1929 and continued until 1931. Among the innovations in this series were four-wheel brakes, left-hand steering, and an automatic cooling system. The powerplant was a 140-horsepower, 6-cylinder, T-head engine.

Yet another American LaFrance merger took place in 1927, when the firm incorporated the O.J. Childs Com-

pany of Utica, New York. The new firm was now officially known as American LaFrance and Foamite Corporation. The Utica plant was closed and all operations were moved to the Elmira site. Childs was primarily a producer of fire protection systems, but the firm had been making some fire apparatus, usually on commercial chassis, since 1923. After the consolidation, American LaFrance produced 51 units of Childs Thoroughbreds; the last was sold in 1928.

American LaFrance attempted, without notable success, to branch out beyond fire engines in the 1920s. A few non-fire vehicles were produced, including some commercial trucks and a number of chief's cars. The building of five T3 tanks based on Christie  prototypes took place at American LaFrance in 1931. The company also experimented with a line of metal playground equipment. Overall, diversification was

not a real success for American LaFrance, and the company soon retreated to its core business of fire engines.

American LaFrance began producing its own excellent engine in 1931. The 12-cylinder, V-block, 240-horsepower engine was a major breakthrough in power plants. Basically two 6-cylinder engines with a common crankshaft, the AFL V-12 was soon powering not just fire apparatus but also buses, trucks and generators. It stayed in production until the early 1960s.

With its reputation for cost-effective, quality equipment, American LaFrance entered the hard times of the 1930s better equipped than most for survival. The short-lived 300 Series apparatus were produced only in 1932 and 1933; these rigs were quickly followed by the 400 Series, produced from 1934 to 1938. The long-hooded Series 400 models had

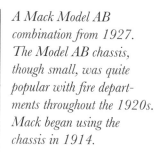

*A Mack Model AB combination from 1927. The Model AB chassis, though small, was quite popular with fire departments throughout the 1920s. Mack began using the chassis in 1914.*

*Mack Model AL rigs were attractive but not particularly popular. This good-looking quad is shown in a factory shot from 1928.*

a low, factory-installed windshield. Several fully enclosed fire engines were built on the Series 400 chassis. This model was also used as the tractor for a very large water tower delivered to Newark, New Jersey, in 1936.

Innovation continued at American LaFrance despite hard times and slow orders. The 65-foot water tower delivered to FDNY in 1930 could pump 8,500 gpm through four nozzles. Aerials with all-hydraulic, four-section metal ladders up to 100 feet long were made available starting in 1938. In 1939, the revolutionary cab-forward, four-wheel aerials were introduced.

An extremely interesting series of apparatus was built for Los Angeles in 1938. These rigs, called Metropolitan Duplexes, had two 240-horsepower, V-12 engines and two two-stage, 1,000-gpm pumps. The front engine drove the apparatus and powered a pump mounted in the cowl. The second engine powered a pump mounted behind the driver's seat. Each Duplex pumper ran with a companion manifold wagon to handle distribution of the output to a maximum of 20 outlets. Two more of these units, this time with 3,000-gpm capacity, were delivered to Los Angeles in 1938. The goal was to reduce the number of rigs and thus the congestion at a major fire; each Duplex pumper

took the place of three conventional pumpers.

The most important development at American LaFrance in the 1930s was the Series 500 apparatus. Offered from 1938 to 1942, these rigs had an attractive, more streamlined look than previous apparatus. Offered with three-man seating and a choice of closed or open cab, the Series 500 sold extremely well. These rigs had two-stage centrifugal pumps mounted in the cowl and V-12 engines. With American entry into World War II and consequent concerns for civil defense, Series 500 apparatus soon became ubiquitous in fire houses.

The war years of the 1940s were challenging, difficult, and profitable for

*Westfield, New Jersey, was served by this 1930 American LaFrance combination. This well-preserved rig has left-hand drive and modern tires.*

most automotive manufacturers. Civilian production of automobiles virtually ceased as factories were devoted strictly to war effort. Although fire engine production was considered vital for national security and continued with only some restrictions, strategic materials such as steel, rubber, and chrome were in short supply. Most fire engines of the period were delivered as bare-minimum models bereft of the shiny chrome so dear to firefighters' hearts.

The Series 600 rigs—basically just improvements and modifications of the Series 500—were offered from 1942 to 1945. Firefighting apparatus for military purposes was also produced in significant quantities. During this time American

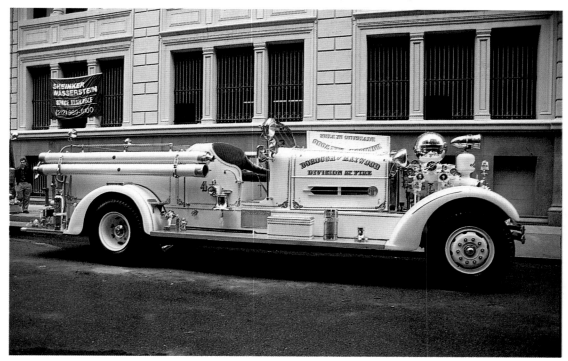

*Engine Company No. 4 of Hackensack, New Jersey was the original owner of this 1938 Ahrens-Fox HT, serial number 3446. The rig is now a parade piece for Maywood, New Jersey.*

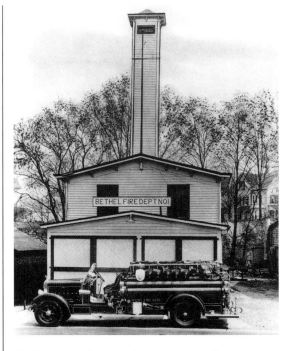

LaFrance also produced aircraft parts, including nosewheel landing-gear spindles and forks and gun-mounting brackets.

## AHRENS-FOX STRUGGLES

The period from 1923 to 1929 is often called the classic era at Ahrens-Fox. During this time, the firm produced some of its finest apparatus and introduced new concepts and designs that were adopted by other manufacturers.

In 1923 Ahrens-Fox delivered its last chain-drive apparatus. Most of the final rigs were part of a 39-piece order for Model Ms from the Chicago fire department. The classic models K and N

stayed in production from 1922 to 1927. Among the many interesting features of these beautiful machines is the right-hand steering. A typical pumper from Ahrens-Fox during this period cost about $13,000.

Ladder truck design achieved a major breakthrough at Ahrens-Fox in this period as well. In 1923, Ahrens introduced the concept of four-wheel, tractor-drawn aerials. The ladders were equipped with Dahill air hoists; 73 had been sold by 1940. Another ladder innovation was double-banked city service ladder trucks. By placing the ground ladders side by side, the center of gravity on the truck was lowered, making the vehicle much more stable when cornering.

The last 4-cylinder Ahrens-Fox was delivered in 1926. From that time on, Ahrens apparatus was powered by 6-cylinder engines. By 1927, the firm was no longer using its own Mooers engine exclusively. Outside engine suppliers such as Waukesha provided an increasingly larger percentage of power plants; by 1939, Ahrens-Fox no longer used its own engines at all.

Yet another design innovation came from Ahrens-Fox in 1928 with the introduction of the light Skirmisher line. This was the first truly integrated approach to the quadruple rig, combining pump, hose, booster tank, and service

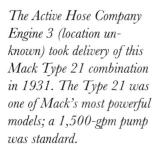

*This busy combination rig went to the City of Jackson (state unknown) in 1931. It is a Mack Type 90. The Type 90 had a 120-horsepower 6-cylinder engine with a 750-gpm pump.*

ladder. The rotary pump was mounted midships and came in 600-gpm and 750-gpm versions.

As the 1930s began, hard times came to Ahrens-Fox. The overall depressed economy meant fewer orders for new apparatus, especially for the pricey Ahrens-Fox models. The firm responded by discontinuing the Model J and offer-ing the less expensive Junior Model V, built on a commercial chassis from the LeBlond-Schacht Truck Company of Cincinnati. At the same time, however, Ahrens introduced the large and expensive Tower Aerial line. This wooden aerial ladder had a tower nozzle mounted on the end. It combined the delivery punch of a water tower with the

*A 1932 Mack Type 50 aerial ladder, built for Stroudsburg, Pennsylvania, in 1932. In this factory photo, the ladder is extended to its full 75-foot length. The Type 50 was one of Mack's smallest models.*

*The Halesite, New York fire department owns this 1925 Ahrens-Fox J-S-2 pumper, serial number 1237. This shot gives a good view of the complicated piston pump.*

*Well-known apparatus collector Alex Black owns this interesting 1929 N-S-3 Ahrens-Fox, serial number 3374. This rig formerly served Lynn, Massachusetts, as Engine 1.*

flexibility and rescue capabilities of an aerial ladder—a concept that would not reach its full potential until steel ladders became usual two decades later.

By 1933 the Model M was no more; by 1935 the famed Model N piston pumper was also discontinued. The rotary-pump, 500-gpm Junior V line was expanded in 1935 and started selling well; more than 50 were sold. Unfortunately, LeBlond-Schacht grew impatient with delayed payments and refused to provide any more chassis. The Junior series died a sudden death as the firm's major creditor nearly paralyzed operations.

*Not all Ahrens-Fox apparatus had a massive front-mounted piston pump. This rig is a 1930 Model GC-60-4 with a rotary pump, left-hand drive, and Clark disk wheels. The serial number is 5049. This apparatus is still owned by the Georgetown, Kentucky department.*

*Engine Company No. 1 of the Vigilant Fire Company in York, Pennsylvania, owned this 1933 Ahrens-Fox C-T-4, serial number 4006. This rig is now in the Maryland Fire Museum.*

LeBlond-Schacht saw a merger with Ahrens-Fox as the only way to collect the money it was owed. With bankruptcy the only alternative, the Ahrens-Fox management agreed in 1936. The decision kept Ahrens-Fox alive and still creative, as shown by the introduction of the magnificent 1000-gpm HT piston pumpers in 1937. These rigs were powered by the Hercules HXE 6-cylinder engine, with a 5¾-inch bore and 6-inch stroke. Twenty-eight were sold to FDNY in the next two years. (In all, 67 HTs were delivered. The final HT went to Tarrytown, New York, in 1952. It was the last piston pumper built by Ahrens-

Fox.) The last Ahrens-Fox aerials ever built, four 85-foot tractor-drawn rigs for FDNY, were delivered in 1940.

The firm's financial position remained shaky, and by 1941 no new Ahrens-Fox apparatus was being built. The LeBlond-Schacht plant was almost totally dedicated to military production. It was not until 1946 that Ahrens-Fox resumed fire engine production, once again selling the popular HT and adding a brilliant new design for a centrifugal pumper.

## MACK CONTINUES TO GROW

The production of fire engines was a small but very successful part of the overall Mack Truck operation by the start of the 1920s. Numerous Mack AC "bulldog" trucks had been used by the military in World War I; these trucks had proven their durability under extremely adverse conditions. The basic design of the AC was so successful that it stayed in production until 1927. The less distinctive Model AB, dating back to 1914, stayed in production for several years longer.

A new line of Mack fire apparatus was introduced starting in 1928, although they did not really begin market penetration until the following year. The larger of these handsome new rigs was designated Type 19. This triple combination pumper was available in 750- and 1,000-gpm versions; the engine was a 150-horsepower, 6-cylinder model. The Type 90 was a smaller rig offered as a 750-gpm straight pumper, city service ladder truck, or double combination.

Starting in 1930, Mack offered even more choices. The Type 70 was a medium-duty design. The Type 50 was a small design that was nevertheless available as a triple combination. The Type 75 had a powerful 140-horsepower, 6-cylinder engine with a 4¼-inch bore and 5½-inch stroke; four-wheel brakes were standard. Buyers had a choice of 750-gpm pumps: rotary gear or centrifugal multistage. The larger Type 95 pumper offered a the same pump choice but added a 1,000-gpm option.

Mack also offered the "Junior" series of smaller, more economical pumpers. The Type 55 had a 100-horsepower engine and a 600-gpm pump. The Type 45 pumped 500 gallons per minute.

Mack's first aerial ladder truck was

*A 140-horsepower motor powered this Mack Type 75 triple combination, delivered in 1936. The pump put out 750 gpm. Buyers could choose between a rotary gear or centrifugal multistage pump.*

*The Mack Type 55 was a smaller model with a 100-horsepower engine. This combination from 1939 includes a water tank.*

introduced in 1929. The ladder, drawn by a Type 90 four-wheel tractor, was raised with an engine-driven hoist. The model was available with 65- or 75-foot ladders.

As enclosed apparatus began to be more popular, Mack carried the idea to an interesting extreme at the behest of

the Charlotte, North Carolina, fire department. The firm created a fully enclosed, sedan-style pumper with a 750-gpm pump.

A new, more streamlined look came in with the Mack Type 80 in 1938. The powerplant was the Mack 168-horsepower Thermodyne. The most powerful

*This 1923 Ahrens-Fox 1,000-gpm pumper served Cincinnati as Engine No. 2.*

Mack pumper ever built, a 1,500-gpm pumper for Wilmington, Delaware, was a Type 21 delivered in 1938. Ten of the 1,000-gpm Type 21 went to New York City in 1944.

Mack continued to produce fire apparatus based on the designs of the 1930s throughout the years of World War II. When the war ended, tremendous pent-up demand for fire apparatus meant a surge in orders. For the first time since the mid-1930s, Mack again began to offer aerial ladders using metal aerials supplied by Maxim. The basic Mack models continued to be very popular. With improvements and modi-

*Stony Brook, New York, owns this 1932 Mack Model B city service truck.*

*This 1937 Mack has a 500-gpm Hale pump. The overhead ladder rack was added in the late 1940s. This rig stayed in service at Attica, New York, well into the 1970s.*

*This Mack Type 45 combination from 1940 has a factory-installed overhead ladder rack. Note the square mesh suction strainer on the rear bumper.*

*Wartime shortages meant that this Mack Type 80 pumper, delivered in 1943, had no chrome trim. The Type 80 had a 168-horsepower Mack Thermodyne engine.*

*This factory photo shows a Seagrave Suburbanite from the 1920s. These small rigs were powered by 70-horsepower Continental engines and usually had 350-gpm pumps. The rigs were popular with smaller departments.*

*This combination ladder/chemical truck was built on a Brockway chassis by Buffalo in 1924. It was delivered to Westhampton Beach, New York.*

fications such as sedan cabs, they were offered well into the 1950s.

## SEAGRAVE AND THE CLOSED CAB

Seagrave had been offering motorized fire apparatus since the distinctive Seagrave AC "buckboards" first appeared in 1910. As the 1920s got underway, Seagrave introduced the small Suburbanite. Powered by a 6-cylinder Continental engine, this popular model had a 350-gpm centrifugal pump; in overall appearance, the Suburbanite was simply a scaled-down version of the standard 750-gpm Seagrave rig. The Suburbanite was an interesting contrast to the Metropolite, Seagrave's largest pumper, which put out 1,300 gpm. In 1926 Seagrave introduced an in-between size, a 600-gpm model called the Special. The improved Sentry model, with 6-cylinder engine, was available by 1931. A standard feature of the Sentry was a factory-installed windshield.

Seagrave continued to supply tractor-drawn water towers and spring-raised aerial ladders throughout the 1920s and into the 1930s. The last Seagrave water tower was massive 65-foot affair for the Washington, D.C., department. By the mid-1930s, aerial ladders from Seagrave were made entirely from metal and were hydraulically raised.

In 1919, most passenger automobiles were open to the elements. By 1924, 43 percent were closed; by 1927, 83 percent were closed. Despite this, it was clear to all fire chiefs of the time that what was desirable to soft civilians in the general public was not appropriate to tough firefighters. Although Pirsch occasionally built some custom apparatus with closed cabs (see below), it was Seagrave who invented the closed canopy cab in 1937. The basic design would remain in production for more than thirty years, superseded only when cab-forward designs became popular.

*In 1925, Buffalo built this triple combination on a REO chassis for Seat Pleasant, Maryland.*

The basic Seagrave canopy cab featured an enclosed forward-facing compartment for the officer and driver; a canopy extended back over a rear-facing bench that could seat three or four firefighters. Seagrave also began offering four-door sedan-style closed cabs. Closed-cab apparatus gradually caught on, but Seagrave continued to deliver some open-cab rigs into the 1940s.

## PETER PIRSCH & SONS: LADDERS AND MORE

As the 1920s began, Peter Pirsch & Sons had a well-deserved reputation for excellent ladders and was also selling fire apparatus built on commercial chassis. By 1926 Pirsch had moved into custom

*A canopy cab sheltered the firemen riding in this 1941 Seagrave, which served Tombstone, Arizona. The engine is a 12-cylinder Pierce-Arrow. The desert sun has faded this nicely preserved rig to a tomato red.*

*Winters, California still keeps this 1940 Buffalo Pathfinder on the reserve roster.*

apparatus powered by Waukesha engines. Pirsch became the first major manufacturer to build a fully enclosed cab on a fire engine. The boxy cab was installed in 1928 on a custom-built pumper that went to Monroe, Wisconsin. Although the enclosed cab concept was a breakthrough, it was not one Pirsch exploited. By the late 1930s, however, Pirsch was delivering the occasional closed-cab pumper.

Pirsch began offering a smaller line of custom pumpers, the Special model, in 1929.
These 90-horsepower rigs were designed for small-town departments; they carried a 500-gpm pump and a large booster tank. A new line of pumpers, with a

*Buffalo used a Larrabee chassis to make this pumper for Boothbay, Maine, in 1926.*

*This 1934 Buffalo 500-gpm pumper served Lake Mohawk, New Jersey.*

choice of centrifugal or rotary pump in a range of capacities, was introduced in 1932 starting with the Model 15. The line went on to include models 14, 16, 19, 20, 21, and 25. The largest was the Model 14, which delivered 1,250 gpm. The most popular was probably the standard Model 20 triple combination with a 500-gpm pump.

Pirsch was famous for outstanding ladder designs, so it was no surprise in 1930 when the company moved into

aerial ladders with the first all-power lifting mechanism. The tractor-drawn Pirsch aerials were raised by two hydraulic lifting cylinders; only one man was required for hoisting. The first delivery was an 85-foot aerial to Spokane, Washington. As the Depression deepened in 1932, Pirsch provided a boon to financially strapped smaller departments by offering a simple, inexpensive aerial hoist that could be retrofitted to existing long ladders. Yet another Pirsch first came in

*The Carnegie Steel factory in Illinois was protected by this 1937 Buffalo pumper.*

*Howe built this little 500-gpm pumper on a Chevrolet chassis in 1938 for Salisbury, North Carolina. Note the siren and warning light mounted above the front bumper.*

1935, when the company delivered America's first 100-foot, all-power metal aerial to Melrose, Massachusetts. The famed Pirsch closed-lattice aluminum ladder was first offered in the late 1930s. Pirsch Junior aerial ladders were popular in the 1930s. The manually raised, two-piece ladder usually extended to 60 or 65 feet. Pirsch weathered the Depression years through the sheer excellence of its established ladder line. During the war years Pirsch, like most other manufacturers, turned to military contracts, but also produced a small number of aerial ladders and custom pumpers. When the war ended, Pirsch returned to fire apparatus.

## THE BARTON PUMP

Starting in 1922, effective, inexpensive fire protection became available to even the smallest, poorest fire departments with the Barton front-mount pump, a small but sturdy unit that took its power from the crankshaft of a truck or car. Easily mounted by any mechanic onto

*FDNY purchased many Ward LaFrance rigs over the years. This closed-cab searchlight truck was delivered in 1937.*

the front of any vehicle (the Model T and—after 1928—the Model A were the natural choices), the centrifugal Barton pump brought modern firefighting to even the most rural areas. The Barton weighed in at only 20 pounds, yet could pump 200 to 250 gpm. It was manufactured by the American Steam Pump Company of Battle Creek, Michigan; this firm, after some mergers, eventually became the American Fire Apparatus Company.

## OTHER MANUFACTURERS: SURVIVAL . . . AND FAILURE

In addition to the well-known names in fire apparatus, a host of smaller firms built equipment in the 1920s. Some, such as Buffalo, were devoted primarily to fire apparatus; others, such as Stutz, built fire rigs on their own chassis as an adjunct to building trucks or cars. Some regional manufacturers, such as Prospect Fire Engine of Prospect, Ohio, produced a fair number of rigs. Not all of the smaller firms survived the Depression; some that did later succumbed to market forces.

*Buffalo.* The Buffalo Fire Extinguishing Manufacturing Company, founded in Buffalo, New York, in 1920, specialized in mounting fire engine bodies on commercial chassis, particularly the Larrabee. The usual version was a basic triple combination with pump, chemical tanks, and ground ladders. In the late 1920s, Buffalo began offering its own custom-built chassis alongside commercial versions. In 1939, Buffalo began offering sedan-style closed cabs and fully enclosed pumpers. Buffalo hung on through the war years, but in 1948 the firm closed its doors.

*Stutz.* The dashing Stutz Bearcat sports car symbolizes the Roaring Twenties to movie-goers, but to fire buffs the name Stutz means outstanding fire engines. Harry Stutz entered the apparatus business in Indianapolis in 1919 with a triple combination pumper. The city promptly placed an order for 35 pieces of motorized apparatus, including pumpers and ten city service ladder trucks. By 1923 the firm offered pumpers as large as 1,200 gpm and as small as the 350-gpm Model K, nicknamed the Baby Stutz. The standard Stutz was the Model C, a 750-gpm triple combination, but Stutz pumpers were available with Northern rotary pumps in capacities ranging 350 gpm to 1,200 gpm. The usual powerplant was a Wisconsin 175-horsepower cam. All told, Stutz produced 235 pumpers, 44 city service ladder trucks, and assorted other pieces, including one tillered aerial.

Stutz did very well at first, but by

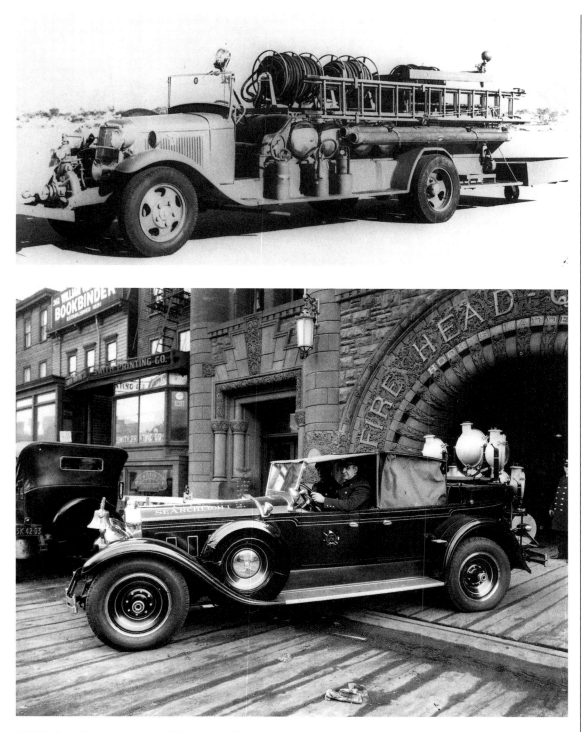

This 1932 Ford open-cab combination pumper and four-tank chemical unit was first used at the Ford Motor Company Airport in Dearborn, Michigan. It was later shipped to the Ford Arizona Proving Grounds.

*This 1932 Ford open-cab combination pumper and four-tank chemical unit was first used at the Ford Motor Company Airport in Dearborn, Michigan. It was later shipped to the Ford Arizona Proving Grounds.*

*FDNY used this 1929 Packard as Searchlight 2. It is shown leaving fire headquarters on Jay Street in Brooklyn.*

1928 the firm was out of business, largely because of internal management problems (Harry Stutz gave his name to the firm at the outset, but soon moved on to other activities). Reorganized as the New Stutz Fire Engine Company, the firm came back in 1931. A few rigs bearing the New Stutz name were produced in the 1930s. The most interesting was the first diesel-powered fire engine ever built, a 1,000-gpm pumper delivered in 1939 to Columbus, Indiana. The engine was a Cummins diesel. By 1940 Stutz was out of business again, this time for good.

*Maxim.* The first Maxim fire apparatus was a motorized hose wagon deliv-

*This 1942 Maxim ladder truck is owned by the West Palm Beach, Florida, fire department.*

*Howe built fire apparatus on Chevrolet chassis fairly often. This 1934 pumper originally served Fort Miley, Georgia, but is now privately owned.*

*Model A Fords were commonly adapted to fire service use. Howe built this little rig for Mount Bethel, New York, in 1928.*

*Oren built this 500-gpm combination with 40-foot ladder on an International Harvester chassis in 1938. It served Hot Springs, Virginia.*

ered in 1914. Although Maxim was primarily a producer of specialty trucks, by 1921 the firm was offering the new M series of 6-cylinder pumpers in various capacities. A new B Model was introduced in 1927; these were available in 750- and 1,000-gpm versions. Maxim apparatus from the early 1920s on through the end of the 1930s is distinguished by a gabled hood and huge radiator. Bolstered by its core truck business, Maxim continued producing fire apparatus throughout the 1930s and 1940s. Another effect of the truck business was that Maxim could offer its fire customers a very wide choice of cabs, including enclosed and canopy styles. By the end of the 1930s, some customers were even ordering them. During the war years, Maxim built a number of military fire engines on commercial chassis.

*Obenchain-Boyer.* The Obenchain-Boyer Company of Logansport, Indiana, specialized in converting commercial chassis to fire use. By concentrating on relatively light, inexpensive chassis from Ford, Dodge, Reo Speedwagon, and other producers, the firm was well established as a favorite of small-town departments by 1918. Obenchain-Boyer was quite successful in the 1920s, but by 1929 the firm was in trouble. It was reorganized as the Boyer Fire Apparatus Company and sold a small but steady number of rigs on commercial chassis into the late 1970s.

*Howe.* The roots of the Howe Fire Apparatus Company go back to 1872. The first motorized pumper from Howe was built in 1907. Howe generally used commercial chassis from Ford, Nash, and other manufacturers to produce light-duty combination rigs for smaller departments. By the 1930s, however, Howe was also offering a line of custom pumpers called Howe Defenders (a name still familiar today). These were originally built on the Defiance chassis, but were later built on a proprietary chassis. Howe continued in business throughout World War II, providing fire engines for both civilian and military use.

*Ward LaFrance.* It's easy to confuse Ward LaFrance with American LaFrance, especially since both firms were once located in Elmira, New York. The two have always been separate companies. Ward LaFrance was originally a maker of truck chassis, but in the 1930s the firm expanded into the custom fire apparatus business. The first rigs were 500- and 750-gpm pumpers. By 1938, nine Ward LaFrance combination hose and turret wagons were in FDNY service. Ward LaFrance continued to build some rigs on commercial chassis, and branched out into airport crash trucks in the 1940s.

*Sanford.* A small but respected apparatus builder was the Sanford Fire Apparatus Company of Syracuse, in the industrial heartland of New York. The firm was founded in 1908 as a truck manufacturer, and remained in that end of the business until the mid-1930s. One Sanford truck model of the early 1920s, the 6-cylinder Greyhound, became a popular chassis for fire engines. In 1925 Sanford entered the apparatus business directly, offering fire engines built on its Model 500 chassis and equipped with Waterous pumps. The firm also continued to assemble rigs on commercial chassis such as the ever-popular Ford TT. Additional custom models were added in the 1920s, including the 500-gpm Model 528 starting in 1928, and the Cub series, introduced in 1929. The Cubs were available in several competitively priced configurations designed for small town use. (A 500-gpm custom pumper from Sanford cost about $6,000 in 1930, as compared to about $7,000 for an equivalent rig from American LaFrance.) This dual strategy of commercial and custom chassis gave the company fair success in selling to smaller municipalities in the Northeast.

Sanford struggled through the Depression years. The Cub series was discontinued in 1933 in favor of the new, more streamline Model 303. Sales were slow, however, and by 1940 the firm was in serious difficulties. The outbreak of World War II brought government orders for apparatus, and the company was able to recover financially and look forward to the postwar years.

*This 1936 Dodge Van Pelt has a front-mounted pump rated at 250 gpm and a 300-gallon water tank. This was the first motorized apparatus of the Rocklin, California, department.*

The first Barton front-mount pump was sold in 1922. These easily installed pumps took their power from the front of the crankshaft; they could be and were mounted on almost any sort of vehicle. The rig shown here is a Ford Model TT straight chemical/hose wagon carrying the original Barton pump. Constructed by Obenchain Boyer, this apparatus originally served Litchfield, Michigan. In 1952 Barton purchased it and used it for promotional purposes. The rig is now in private hands.

Typical of the hundreds of pumpers delivered by Oren in the 1930s and 1940s is this 1938 rig built on a Ford chassis.

*This stubby-looking 1942 Sanborn is built on a rare Ford cab-over-engine chassis with extended crew cab.*

FIRE ENGINES

## Chapter Five

# From Civil Defense to Civil Disturbance

For the fire service as for everyone else, the world was a very different place after World War II. Significant new concepts in equipment and methods, combined with rapidly expanding suburbs, led to new growth in fire departments and new demand for apparatus. In the 1950s new cab-forward designs changed the appearance of fire apparatus forever. The advent of practical diesel powerplants, improved radio communications, metal aerials, elevating platforms, and other technological changes of the 1950s and 1960s led to greatly improved efficiency and safety. Civil unrest and attacks on firefighters in the 1960s ended open cabs.

## THE CAB-FORWARD REVOLUTION

Designers at American LaFrance had come up with a radical new approach to the basic design of a fire engine as early as 1944. The cab-forward design, as it came to be called, placed the cab of the apparatus directly ahead of the standard V-12 engine, giving the rig a sleek, snub-nosed look. Appearances aside, the cab-forward design also reduced the turning radius and greatly aided visibility for the chauffeur. The entire design was com-

pact, efficient, and maneuverable. By placing the engine behind the cab, the engineers could link it directly to the centrifugal pump. The new cab—whether open, semi-open, or closed—seated three comfortably. Another two firefighters could ride on side seats on either side of the engine compartment, while another three firefighters could ride the rear step.

Wartime exigencies put the cab-forward design on hold. By 1947, however, American LaFrance was ready to introduce Series 700 apparatus. The very first deliveries were two 1,250-gpm closed-cab pumpers to Elkhart, Indiana. The first aerial on the new model was a closed-cab 85-footer for Binghamton, New York. (Aerials in the 700 series came as four-wheel or tractor models.) The first big order came from FDNY: 20 open-cab, 750-gpm pumpers with turret pipes and subway hangers on the rear step.

The new design found a ready market. A large backlog of orders from the war years, when few departments could convince the authorities that they absolutely had to have a new fire engines, was filled with Series 700 apparatus. Expanding departments nationwide

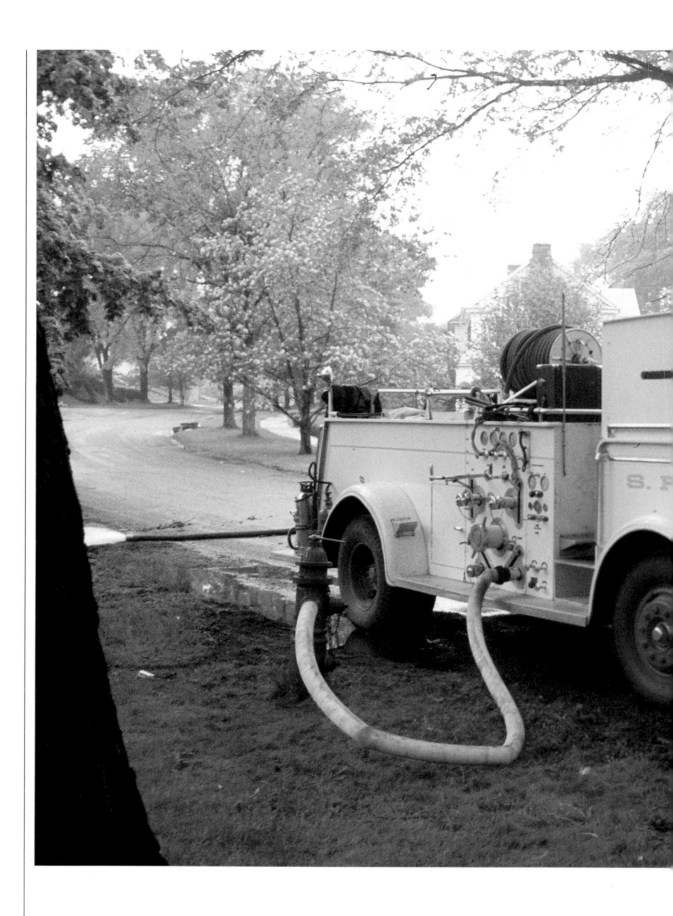

clamored for the new rigs, to the point that American LaFrance soon turned its entire production line over to the Series 700 models. By 1948, over 800 pieces of assorted apparatus on the Series 700 design had been sold. A typical Series 700 rig of the period was a quadruple combination carrying a 500-gpm pump, booster tank, hose, and ground ladders. A choice of V-12 engines was offered.

On larger apparatus such as aerials, quints, or 1,000-gpm pumpers, the standard engine was the American LaFrance J model, a V-12 delivering 215 horsepower. In 1955, a line of smaller, less expensive Series 700 models developed for rural and small-town departments. The Ranger, Protector, and Crusader lines were all introduced in 1955. Available with pump sizes ranging

from 500 to 1,000 gpm, these models were powered by 6-cylinder in-line engines from Continental.

The major plant investment required to retool for cab-forward production had placed American LaFrance in a difficult financial position despite healthy sales. To finance additional growth and ongoing research and development, in 1956 the firm was sold to Sterling Preci-

sion Corporation.

Successful as the Series 700 was, there was still room for improvement. The Series 800 models, introduced in 1956, offered a choice of seven different engines, open or closed cab, and an improved centrifugal pump, as well as some cosmetic changes.

In 1958, the Series 800 line was replaced by the remodeled and improved

Series 900 line. More streamlined and with a wraparound windshield, the Series 900 became extremely popular and remained in production until the late 1970s. Buyers could opt for an open or canopy cab and choose among eight different engines.

The Series 900 chassis was in 1960 used for one of the odder experiments in fire history: turbine-powered fire engines. These unusual rigs were powered by a 325-horsepower jet engine from Boeing. Only a few were ever made, including a 1,000-gpm triple combination pumper with semi-open cab for San Francisco and a 100-foot tractor-drawn aerial for Seattle. The experiment was a dismal failure. The rigs were noisy, slow

*This stylish all-black American LaFrance rig is a Series 700 from 1950.*

*A 1957 American LaFrance 100-foot ladder truck in action at a fire in Syracuse, New York in 1967. Syracuse apparatus was traditionally painted white.*

to accelerate, and hard to brake. All were quickly converted to conventional gasoline power.

In 1965 the 900 Series became the first custom chassis from American LaFrance to offer diesel power. American LaFrance, along with Mack, was again a pioneer in the area. Within a few years, diesel had become the powerplant of choice for fire apparatus. Diesel engines are simple, sturdy, and reliable; they operate on cheaper fuel; and they are more efficient for powering large, heavy apparatus. (Gasoline engines continue to be used on many smaller rigs built on commercial chassis.)

American LaFrance began offering a low-cost line of custom pumpers called

*Bardstown, Kentucky owns this 1958 American LaFrance Series 900 rig. The pump generates 750 gpm. Note the overhead ladder rack and the Civil Defense emblem above the front wheel.*

the Pioneer in 1964. Somewhat boxy in appearance, with a forward-raked windshield on the five-man canopy cab, these rigs were fairly popular with smaller departments. The basic design stayed in production until 1971.

In 1966 American LaFrance once again changed hands, becoming a division of A-T-O Inc., formerly known as "Automatic" Sprinkler. In 1963, the near-bankrupt "Automatic" Sprinkler Company had been purchased by a group of investors led by Harry E. Figgie, Jr. Thus American LaFrance became, and still remains, part of Figgie International.

## AHRENS-FOX GOES UNDER

Ahrens-Fox returned to building fire engines in 1946, offering both piston (Model HT) and centrifugal (Models HC and VC) pumps. Despite an excellent redesign for the centrifugal pumpers (the near-perfect HT piston pumper could not really be improved upon), orders were slow. Production of those orders that did come in was given a low priority

at the LeBlond-Schacht plant. Only 18 rigs were made in 1947. Things improved a little in 1948, with 38 rigs sold. By 1949 the number had dropped to 26; by 1950 it was eight. Clearly, this was not the way to stay in business.

A reorganization in 1950 made Ahrens-Fox a division of the Cleveland Automatic Machine Company, owned by Harold LeBlond. In 1951, Ahrens-Fox delivered only two fire engines. The division was hurriedly sold the same year to General Truck Sales Corporation of Cincinnati, a distributor for General Motors. General Truck thought that the best way to revive the company would be to build 750-gpm pumpers on commercial GMC truck chassis. This would, in theory, bring the price of an Ahrens-Fox fire engine within the reach of even small departments. In all, 16 of these pumpers were actually built and sold, all with centrifugal pumps. No amount of retrofitting could force the famed front-mounted Ahrens-Fox piston pump into a midships position on a GMC chassis.

By 1952, the centennial year for

*FDNY Rescue Company received this custom-built Mack rescue truck in 1948. Mack called it a Type 75S.*

*This 1947 750-gpm American LaFrance Series 700 pumper protected Proctor, Vermont. It is now privately owned.*

Ahrens-Fox, the firm was barely hanging on. Only six custom rigs were made, including the very last two HT piston pumpers Ahrens-Fox ever built. Sales were scarcely better in 1953, and General Truck filed for bankruptcy. Ahrens-Fox was sold again. This time the optimistic buyer was the C.D. Beck Company, a firm best known for building buses. Beck itself was not on the firmest footing, and quality and deadlines slipped. Few expected that Ahrens-Fox would survive beyond delivering whatever orders were on hand.

Surprisingly, after this change Ahrens-Fox did not slide quietly into

oblivion. In 1955 the firm introduced an excellent new cab-forward design based in part on the bus designs in use at Beck. As the only real competition to American LaFrance's cab-forward design, the new concept was well received in the industry. Sadly, only a handful were ever built under the Ahrens-Fox/Beck name. The last fire engine ever with an Ahrens-Fox nameplate was a cab-forward design with a 750-gpm centrifugal pump delivered to Northern Hills, Ohio, in 1958. This rig, delivered with an open semi-cab and a deluge gun, was Model ECB-750, serial number 2006.

C.D. Beck was purchased by Mack

An unusual array of warning devices adorns the front of this American LaFrance Series 700 85-foot aerial ladder. A red 360-degree rotating beacon is on the roof; four large red lights are arranged across the front below the windshield; two small red lights are positioned below the headlights; a motor-driven siren with a red light is on the driver's side; a large bell is on the officer's side; large Grover air horns are mounted on the roof; dual electronic sirens are on the front bumper.

*This Mack Type 21 pumper was delivered in 1950.*

*Grosse Pointe Farms, a suburb of Detroit, received this Mack Type 85LS aerial ladder in 1951.*

FIRE ENGINES

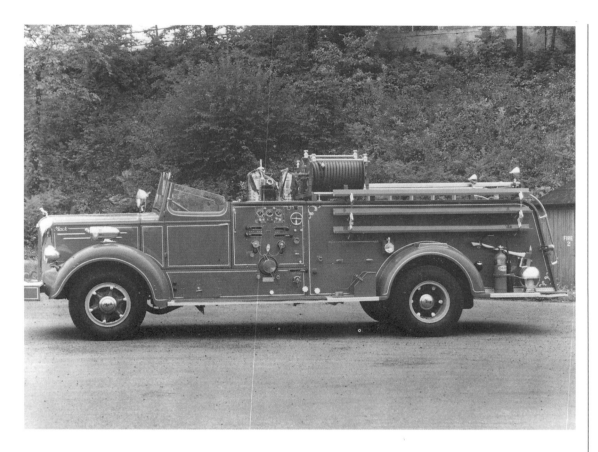

Trucks in 1956. Some assembly of remaining Ahrens-Fox/Beck orders took place at the former Beck plant, alongside Mack trucks and buses. By 1958, the Model FCB Fox cab-forward design, with some modifications, had been taken over by Mack and was being successfully marketed as the Mack C-85. Ahrens-Fox was no more.

## MACK FIRE APPARATUS

The expression "built like a Mack truck" came from the solid performance of these vehicles during World War I. Mack trucks contributed to victory in World War II as well, leaving the firm well positioned for the transition back to civilian production.

One major advantage at Mack was that some fire apparatus production had continued throughout the war years. In 1941 New York took delivery of a dozen 1,000-gpm Type 21 pumpers, and added another ten in 1944.

When peacetime production resumed in full, Mack was offering several popular models: the Type 45 500-gpm pumper; the Type 75 750-gpm pumper with open cab; the Type 85 750-gpm pumper with closed cab; and the Type 95 1,000-gpm pumper. The Type 19 was also in great demand. New York purchased 25 1,000-gpm Type 19 pumpers in 1953. In 1950 the St. Paul, Minnesota fire department purchased 14 Type 95 triple combination pumpers; in 1954 Chicago purchased 30 Type 95 double combination pumpers.

In 1954 Mack announced the completely new B Model. Powered by the 6-cylinder overhead-valve Mack Thermodyne engine, the B Models were powerful and sturdy. They were available in a wide range of cab configurations; pumps ranging from 500 to 1,250 gpm were offered. Mack also offered a

*This 1968 American
LaFrance Series 900 runs
in Miami, Florida.*

*Springfield, Kentucky owns
this 1969 American
LaFrance Pioneer 1,000-
gpm pumper. Fully
equipped, it cost $29,500.*

FIRE ENGINES

The business end of an Ahrens-Fox HT pumper. This is a 1950 delivery to Highland, New York, serial number 3483.

*Boston purchased a number of these Mack Model B rigs in 1956 and 1957. Note the three-way turret pipe connection to the right of the pump panel and the canted ladder. These rigs pumped 1,250 gpm.*

*FDNY received this 1,000-gpm Mack C95F in 1958 as part of an order of twelve.*

six-wheel, tractor-drawn aerial on the B Model. By this time Mack no longer manufactured ladders; the ladders on these rigs came from Maxim and from Magirus. The B Model became a bestseller for Mack and remained in production until 1967.

When Mack purchased C.D. Beck in 1956, the apparent corporate reason was to break into bus manufacture with an established design; Ahrens-Fox fire engines were a minor aspect of the acquisition. The bus business flopped for Mack, but the cab-forward fire engine design obtained in the purchase went on to become the highly successful C-85

and C-95 cab-forward models. The C-85 rigs had 750-gpm pumps, while the C-95 rigs had 1,000-gpm pumps. Both versions were powered by 6-cylinder Mack Thermodyne engines. Automatic transmission was an option.

In 1957, the Beck plant in Ohio was closed and all production was moved to Mack's headquarters in Allentown, Pennsylvania. The factory promptly got busy on the first big order for C Series rigs: 44 pumpers for FDNY, part of a major upgrade program that sent 52 C-85 pumpers and 12 C-95 pumpers to New York in 1958. In 1959, FDNY took delivery of seven C-85s and 13 C-95s. All of these rigs had automatic transmissions, the first ever used in New York. All also had 1,250-gpm deluge guns mounted on their roofs. FDNY purchased 13 C-85F tractor-drawn aerial ladder trucks in 1959. On 11 rigs, the 85-foot ladders were manufactured by Maxim; the other two used 100-foot ladders from Magirus.

Mack had been experimenting with diesel power since the late 1950s. A few deliveries of diesel-powered rigs took place in the early sixties, but it wasn't until 1964 that a convincing demonstration of diesel's worth took place. At a pumping test in Detroit, a Mack C-95 1,000-gpm diesel-powered pumper worked continuously for seven full days.

*A sporty rag top ornaments this Mack Type 85 1952 pumper.*

*The unusual tan color of this 1965 Mack C95 1,000-gpm pumper is traditional for the Mount Holly, New Jersey department.*

Syracuse, New York,
purchased three Seagrave
fully enclosed 1,000-gpm
pumpers in 1947.

This 1953 Seagrave 75-
foot ladder truck served
Baltimore, Maryland.

At the end of the trial, the pumper had moved more than ten million gallons of water and used only about 1,100 gallons of diesel fuel. Soon most Mack fire apparatus was being sold with Thermodyne diesel engines. In 1965, FDNY took delivery of ten diesel-powered 1,000-gpm C-95 pumpers; thereafter, diesel power was standard in the department.

One problem with cab-forward apparatus is access to the engine compartment for servicing. At first, removable panels were added inside the cab. In 1949, White Motors introduced the first tilt-cab chassis. This innovative concept allowed access to the engine by literally tilting the cab forward. The concept quickly caught on. In 1958 Mack introduced its first tilt-cab truck models, the N Series, using a chassis built by the Budd Company. This was followed in 1962 by the F series, which remained in production until the early 1980s. Another popular Mack tilt-cab chassis was the MB Series, introduced in the mid-1960s. This chassis was exceptionally maneuverable, which made it ideal for city service fire apparatus.

SEAGRAVE

In 1947, Seagrave introduced a new version of the short canopy cab the firm had been offering since 1937. The new cabs had small, usually oval, side windows and a V-shaped windshield; the design stayed in production at Seagrave until the end of the 1950s. The basic canopy-cab concept would be adopted by other manufacturers as closed apparatus started to become standard. Seagrave also continued to offer its Safety Sedan fully enclosed pumper. The primary customer for these 1,000-gpm rigs was the Detroit fire department, which purchased its first Safety Sedans in 1936 and its last in 1960. A few Safety Sedans were sold to other departments in the 1940s and early 1950s.

Seagrave celebrated its 70th anniversary in 1951. To commemorate the event, Seagrave introduced a new line of fire engines called the 70th Anniversary Series—a line so successful it stayed in production until 1970. The Anniversary Series rigs were streamlined and modern-looking with built-in equipment storage boxes on the rear fenders, but they retained many proven elements of older designs. In particular, they remained engine-ahead models equipped with Seagrave V-12 engines and centrifugal pumps. A highly visible feature of the Anniversary series rigs is the siren built into the nose of the truck.

Although Anniversary Series apparatus continued to sell well throughout the 1950s, it was apparent to Seagrave that a cab-forward model was needed. It was not until 1959, however, that the first cab-forward chassis was offered. It soon became even more popular than the Anniversary model.

In 1956, the Maxim Motor Company was wholly acquired by Seagrave. The two companies continue to operate as separate units. Seagrave was well-known for aerial ladders before the Maxim purchase; after the purchase, the aerial ladder business became and remained even stronger. Maxim began offering an attractive cab-forward line of its own in 1959, the Model F. This too became quite popular and stayed in production well into the 1970s.

Seagrave and Maxim were purchased in 1963 by the Four Wheel Drive Corporation and became known as the Seagrave Fire Apparatus Division. Production was moved from the Columbus, Ohio, plant to the FWD plant in Clintonville, Wisconsin.

The Mack Model N used the Budd tilt cab, which would become far better known as the cab on the extremely popular Ford C Series chassis. This floodlight truck was delivered to Hicksville, New York, in 1961.

Lexington, Kentucky, received this Maxim 750-gpm combination rig with extended canopy cab in 1950.

*Syracuse purchased three more 1,000-gpm Seagraves in 1953. The open cabs were later closed in with homemade covers.*

FIRE ENGINES

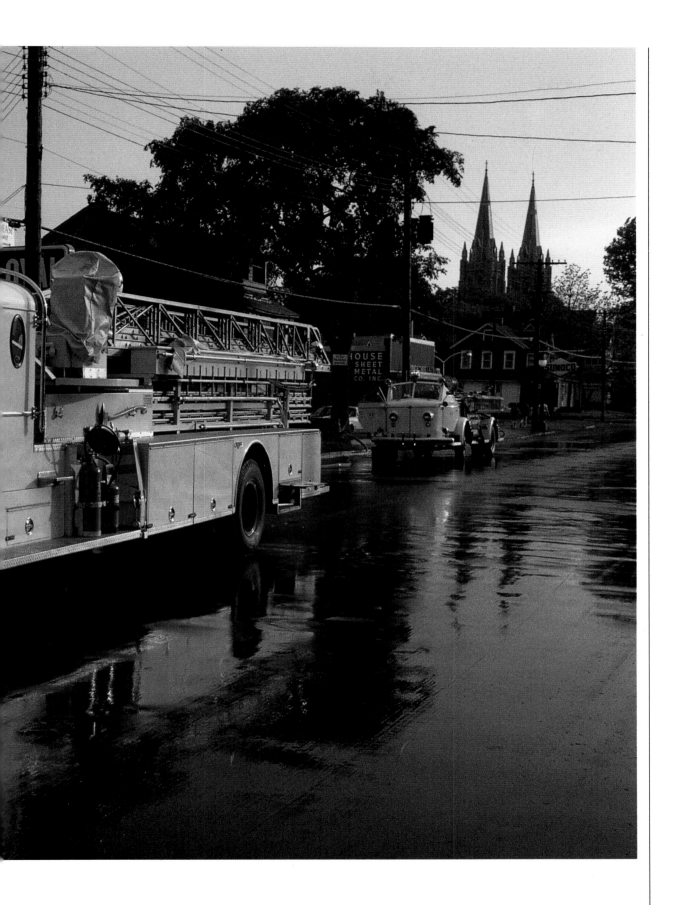

## THE CIVIL DEFENSE PROGRAM

Cold War fears in the early 1950s led to the creation of a federally funded Civil Defense program that provided many municipalities with money for new fire apparatus. The fire apparatus purchased through the program, which ran through the mid-1950s, carried the words "Civil Defense" and a blue triangular emblem. The program did provide a number of cities with new apparatus, but it was not particularly generous. FDNY, for example, estimated that hundreds more pumpers and ladder trucks would be needed to fight fires in New York City in the event of nuclear attack. Perhaps because the federal government was given to wishful thinking (it also thought that "duck and cover" would be a useful procedure), the department received funding for only 65 pumpers. Inadequate as it was, the Civil Defense program did help pay for badly needed apparatus in areas deemed likely bomb targets.

## OTHER FIRE APPARATUS IN THE FIFTIES

Big firms such as Mack and American LaFrance seized a large share of the market for new fire apparatus in the postwar period, forcing some struggling producers out of business. By 1948, for example, Buffalo was gone. The apparatus market was far from closed to new ventures, however, and a number of firms remained profitable or successfully entered the arena in the 1950s. A few of the best-known manufacturers are discussed below.

*Howe.* The sturdy Howe Defenders of the 1930s got a new look in 1953, when the firm began building them on a new, larger chassis powered by a Waukesha 6-cylinder engine. These were big rigs, offered only in 750- 1,000- and 1,250-gpm configurations. In 1960, Howe

*A 65-foot ladder is on this 1955 Maxim quint. This 750-gpm rig went to Owings Mills, Maryland.*

started offering the Defender on a new, five-man cab-forward chassis made by Truck Cab Manufacturers of Cincinnati. The canopy cab on this model was so well designed that it was soon adopted by virtually every apparatus builder. Hence the style came to be known as the Cincinnati cab, even when it was manufactured elsewhere. Howe delivered a number of custom Defenders with the new design, but apparatus on commercial chassis continued to be the firm's chief business.

Howe began offering a raised pump control panel in 1967. Instead of putting the pump operator's control panel in its traditional place on the right side of the truck, Howe placed the panel transversely above the back of the cab. This gave the pump operator a full view of the fire ground. Despite its obvious advantages, the elevated pump panel didn't really catch on until twenty years later.

*Pirsch.* Peter Pirsch & Sons Company survived the war years well and found a ready civilian market for its products in the postwar period. Pirsch had always been particularly well-regarded for ladder-equipped apparatus. Beginning in 1948, the firm offered a small aerial ladder truck designated the Junior model. These rigs were stripped-down versions of Pirsch's larger designs. The ladders were short—in the 55-foot range—and were manually raised. The price was low, and soon many smaller departments were purchasing their first aerial trucks.

Throughout the 1950s and 1960s, Pirsch continued to build aerial ladders and combination fire engines on both custom and commercial chassis.

*Ward LaFrance.* Just after the war, Ward LaFrance received an order from FDNY for 20 750-gpm pumpers. The

*The last Seagrave pumper to come from the Columbus, Ohio, plant was this 1963 1,250-gpm rig with 500-gallon water tank. It is now owned by the Wilcox, Arizona, fire department.*

*This well-preserved 1949 750-gpm Seagrave is now owned by a private collector.*

*This fully enclosed 1,000-gpm Seagrave was delivered to Tarrytown, New York, in 1963.*

*Endicott, New York, took delivery of this 1,250-gpm Seagrave combination with jazzy rag top in 1967.*

*Motorized Apparatus Since 1900*

Hoboken, New Jersey,
received this Maxim Model
S with 100-foot Magirus
ladder in 1961.

first was delivered in 1946. FDNY was partial to Ward LaFrance apparatus; another 25 pumpers went to the department in 1954 as part of a Civil Defense purchase.

In 1949, Ward LaFrance began offering a new production model called the Elmira Eagle. Available in 500- and 750-gpm versions, this new model had an optional three-man closed cab. It was offered throughout the 1950s, and hundreds were sold.

The restyled Fireball Special series from Ward LaFrance was offered in 1954. The basic design was not all that different from earlier versions; the price remained very attractive. A 500-gallon booster tank was standard equipment. These small pumpers sold well to rural and suburban departments.

Ward LaFrance began selling aerial ladder trucks in 1955. The ladders came

from Maxim. Buyers could choose between four-wheel service trucks or tractor-drawn models.

It was not until 1960 that Ward LaFrance came out with a cab-forward model, the Premium. Variations on the basic idea were offered from that time onward, although conventional engine-ahead models remained in production.

*FMC.* The John Bean Division of the Food Machinery Corporation (better known today as FMC) began offering high-pressure fog systems mounted on commercial chassis in the late 1920s. The basis of the system was the high-pressure spray pump John Bean had developed for agricultural use.

High-pressure fog was a very effective firefighting technique that was much further developed during the war, primarily to fight shipboard and airport fires. FMC built a number of fog-

*This Maxim Model F with 750-gpm pump was delivered to the Luzerne-Hadley Fire Department in New York in 1963.*

*A Maxim Model S with deck gun went to Hoboken, New Jersey, around 1961.*

*A 1967 Seagrave 1,000-gpm pumper at work in Syracuse, New York, shortly after it was delivered.*

*This 1949 Maxim four-door cab pumper was delivered to Harrisville, Rhode Island. The pump capacity was 750 gpm.*

FIRE ENGINES

*This 1968 Maxim 85-foot tillered aerial stayed in first-line service in Lancaster, Ohio, until the 1980s.*

*This 1948 Ward LaFrance 750-gpm pumper is owned by the Rio Vista Fire Department in California. The engine is a 6-cylinder Waukesha; the pump is from Waterous.*

*The Ford Research and Engineering Center in Dearborn, Michigan, was protected by this 1957 Ford/Howe 750-gpm pumper.*

*A 1957 factory delivery shot shows a Pirsch/Ford 85-foot aerial for Decatur, Georgia.*

FIRE ENGINES

equipped airport crash trucks for military use during World War II. When fog was applied to civilian firefighting, it proved equally effective in the right circumstances. Among other advantages, fog requires far less water than conventional methods and thus causes less water damage and less strain on the water supply. FMC built primarily fog-equipped apparatus, but also put together some conventional rigs.

*Crown Body & Coach.* Primarily a builder of buses, Crown entered the fire apparatus market in 1949 with a custom-built 1,250-gpm pumper delivered to West Covina, California. Because Crown had extensive experience with bus designs, the company's fire apparatus were cab-forward models from the beginning.

Crown was and remains based in Los Angeles, California, and its equipment is sold primarily on the West Coast. The Los Angeles City Fire Department is a big user of Crown apparatus. In 1963, the department purchased two massive Coach fire engines. One rig was a gigantic manifold wagon with a 2,000-gpm pump, 14 outlets for 2½-inch hose, and a hydraulically operated Stang turret pipe. The other rig was a 2,000-gpm pumper with a massive Greenburg deck monitor.

Crown's own custom apparatus carries the Firecoach model name. Because Los Angeles uses so many of them (the department has purchased nearly 300 over the years), Crown rigs have received wide exposure on television shows filmed in the area.

## THE SUPER PUMPER

One of the most unusual and famous pieces of fire apparatus ever built was delivered in 1965 to FDNY by Mack Trucks. Dubbed the Super Pumper, this feat of engineering was an incredibly powerful pumping engine that was designed to take the place of ten ordinary pumpers. The idea was to have one rig that could pump massive amounts of water onto the sort of major fire that might be expected in New York City's skyscraper territory. Planning began in 1963; the total cost was over $875,000.

The Super Pumper was hauled by a three-axle Mack F Series diesel tractor. The giant pump was carried on the semitrailer. The engine was a Napier-Deltic diesel rated at 2,400 horsepower at 1,800 rpm; it weighed 13,000 pounds. The engine was coupled directly to the DeLaval Turbine 6-stage centrifugal pump. This huge pump was capable of delivering an incredible 8,800 gpm at 350 psi, drawing from as many as eight hydrants. At 4,400 gpm, the Super Pumper produced 700 psi; at 10,000 gpm, it produced 300 psi. When running at full blast, the Super Pumper used nearly 140 gallons of diesel fuel in an hour; the total fuel capacity was 400 gallons. The unit was 43 feet long, eight feet wide, and just over 11 feet high. The gross weight was 68,500 pounds. With the exception of fireboats, no more powerful fire apparatus has ever been built.

The Super Pumper was accompanied by the Super Tender, which started out with an 8-inch, 10,000-gpm McIntyre monitor and carried 2,000 feet of 4½-inch hose. The monitor was an immediate problem. Before the Super Tender went into service, it was replaced with an 8-inch Stang monitor.

The Super Pumper and the Super Tender were accompanied by three C Series Satellite Tenders, each with a 6-inch, 4,000-gpm Stang monitor and 2,000 feet of hose. Each monitor was supplied by four 4½-inch inlets.

This nicely preserved 1954
Ward LaFrance pumper
with rag top has a 750-gpm
pump. The rig belongs to
Nanuet, New York.

This dramatic shot shows a Pirsch 85-foot aerial ladder at a fire in Toledo, Ohio.

*This 1958 Ward LaFrance Fireball with open cab protected Binghamton, New York.*

*A Hi Ranger 85-foot snorkel is carried on this 1965 Ward LaFrance. The rig served Savannah, Georgia.*

The amazing Super Pumper remained in service until 1982, when the aging units were replaced by no fewer than six double units of 2,000-gpm pumpers and accompanying hose wagons.

## THE SNORKEL

One day in 1958, Chicago Fire Commissioner Robert Quinn happened to notice some city workers cleaning an overhead sign. The workers were using a cherrypicker—an articulated boom with a bucket large enough to hold two men, mounted on the back of a small truck. Quinn was struck by the ease with which the workers could maneuver into position, and had the original and brilliant

This 1957 Pirsch 1,000-gpm pumper carries its hard suction hose in a squirrel tail.

This 1948 Buffalo Sedan Cab pumper is typical of the last rigs this manufacturer built.

idea of using the same concept for firefighting. Quinn's insight was sharpened by the knowledge that the department's three antiquated water towers needed to be replaced.

Because the cherrypicker concept had been around since 1951, the Chicago department's shop was able to purchase a 50-foot articulated boom with basket from the Pitman Manufacturing Company in Missouri and mount it on an ordinary truck chassis. A length of hose was placed alongside the boom and attached to a 2-inch nozzle in the basket; the final result produced 1,200 gpm at up to 100 psi. This, the first elevating platform in the fire service, has gone down in history by the name of

Quinn's Snorkel. The legendary source of the name comes from the new device's first use. In October, 1958, a month after it was placed in service, the rig was called out for a four-alarm lumberyard fire. It was spectacularly effective, dousing the blaze in short order. Speaking with reporters afterward, the firefighter operating the basket hose dubbed the rig "Commissioner Quinn's snorkel," because he had been under the water from the streams of other rigs the entire time. The name stuck, and Commissioner Quinn became widely known by the less dignified name Snorkel Bob.

The snorkel received wide publicity and praise after it was used to fight the tragic Our Lady of Angels school fire on 1 December 1958. This fire, which occurred in an unsprinklered building with open stairwells, took the lives of 92 children and three teachers. The snorkel was featured in the photographs of the disaster that appeared on the front pages of newspapers across the nation.

The Pitman Company quickly capitalized on its head start in the elevating platform business, but other firms soon joined the competition. The Snorkel Fire Equipment Company was formed in St. Joseph, Missouri. In addition to standard elevating platforms on articulated booms, telescoping booms for use in constricted spaces were developed. The Snorkel Company came up with a combination water tower and aerial ladder on telescoping boom. These models, the Squrt and the Telesqurt, could be mounted on pumpers, giving a new twist to the combination concept.

Along with the development of the snorkel came major improvements in aerial ladders. The standard aerial truck by the early 1950s was a four-wheel chassis carrying a multiple-section, hydraulically operated, all-metal ladder driven by a power take-off from the transmission and stabilized by extendable jacks. Rear-mounted ladders, with their increased maneuverability, became popular in the 1960s.

## AN ERA ENDS

As the turbulent 1960s went on, firefighters became the targets of attack in depressed urban areas. Rocks, Molotov cocktails, and worse were thrown at firefighters riding in exposed positions on the trucks. The tragic civil disturbances that punctuated the late sixties ended open cabs and made riding the rear step a thing of the past. Existing apparatus was often modified locally to close in the cabs and provide protection to the rear steps and the hose beds. By this point, although closed cabs were virtually standard on all new apparatus anyway, few chiefs could have had any lingering doubts about ordering them.

As the 1960s drew to an end, the fire service could look back on more than 25 years of improvement and growth. Fire apparatus had become bigger, faster, more powerful, and more efficient. Radio communications had become nearly universal, and new concepts such as the elevating platform had given firefighters powerful new tools to fight an old enemy. The era came to its true close in 1972, when FDNY added its one thousandth motorized pumper to the roster.

FD.NY's amazing Super Pumper on parade around 1967. This enormous rig was hauled by a Mack F Series diesel tractor.

Hope Valley, Rhode Island received this Ford 750-gpm quint in 1969. This truck carried a full assortment of ground ladders

*Sanford built this 750-gpm pumper on a Brockway chassis in 1949.*

*The Port Authority of New York and New Jersey operated this odd little rig in the Holland Tunnel in the 1950s. It was designed to operate forward and backward.*

*Part of the huge DeLaval pump can be glimpsed in this nice view of the FDNY Super Pumper.*

*The Super Tender with its gigantic Stang monitor and huge hose bed can be seen in this shot.*

FIRE ENGINES

*FDNY's Super Tender and three Satellite Tenders demonstrate their abilities at a drill in the late 1960s. The UN building is in the background.*

*The F.D.N.Y. Super Pumper system was retired in 1982 and later sold. The Super Tender is now in private hands and undergoing restoration. Here the newly installed monitor—not yet painted—is tested.*

*A head-on view of a 1972 Crown 100-foot ladder truck. This rig is ex-Orange County, California.*

The original Snorkel No. 1 was retired from the Chicago Fire Department in the condition shown here. The Snorkel Economy Company purchased the dilapidated rig and restored it in 1988.

The refurbished Snorkel No. 1 was taken back to Chicago in 1988 and demonstrated there.

*This 1994 100-foot aerial platform from Pierce also carries a 200-gallon water tank, a 1,500-gpm two-stage pump, and a 450-horsepower engine.*

FIRE ENGINES

# Chapter Six

# The Modern Era

As the 1970s began, the fundamental designs of most fire apparatus were well established. The changes to come in the next decades were primarily for increased firefighter safety and comfort—improvements and refinements, not radical innovation.

THE MAJOR MANUFACTURERS
Many of the chief producers of fire apparatus at the end of the 1960s continue to be strong in the market today. A few have dropped out of the business or reduced their presence—and a few new names have entered the market.

*American LaFrance.* The American LaFrance Series 900 models were joined in 1970 by the Series 1000 versions, which featured standard diesel power. In 1973 the Century Series of custom apparatus was introduced. Incorporating many of the standard features of the Series 1000 rigs, the Century Series offered a redesigned cab and improved visibility. The Stinger line of quick-attack pumpers, targeted to rural and village departments, began in 1975. Built on Chevrolet or Dodge 4 x 4 chassis, they were equipped with 250-gpm pumps and 250-gallon stainless steel water tanks. Another commercial pumper line, the

Spartan, was introduced in 1976. This budget-priced rig had seating for five crew members. Options included a choice of diesel or gasoline engine, 500- or 750-gpm water tank, and pump capacity ranging from 750 to 1,250 gpm. Other new models from American LaFrance in the 1970s included the Challenger/Conquest line in 1978, the 100-foot Water Chief aerial ladder in 1976, and the 75-foot Water Chief aerial ladder in 1979.

In the 1980s American LaFrance was moved from Elmira, New York, to Bluefield, Virginia. At the same time, American LaFrance made its first delivery of apparatus in 30 years to FDNY: 80 1,000-gpm pumpers in 1981, nine more in 1982, and 14 in 1984.

Current offerings from American LaFrance include the Pioneer line of budget-priced commercial pumpers, the Pacemaker commercial pumpers, and the Century 2000 custom line.

The Pioneer line offers a 1,250-gpm Twinflow pump, four-man tilt cab, and 240-hp Cummins diesel engine. The Pacemaker is built on a Pemfab tilt-cab chassis. A typical pumper in this line has a 1,500-gpm Hale pump, a 500-gallon fiberglass water tank, a 300- or 350-hp

*Palm Beach Gardens, Florida, runs this 1970 American LaFrance aerial tower.*

*This 1972 American LaFrance Pioneer has a 1,250-gpm pump. It is on the roster of Saranac, New York, as Engine 316.*

diesel engine, and seats six. This chassis can also be equipped with Squrt or Telesqurt articulating elevating platforms from Snorkel.

In the early 1990s American LaFrance added two more lines: the Patriot, a moderately priced commercial pumper, and World Class vehicles. The Patriot features stainless steel tilt cabs seating six to ten firefighters. An additional rear cab module with either high headroom or low profile is available. Roll-up compartments, stainless-steel body, and polypropelene water tanks are other features. Buyers can select a Twinflow or Hale pump in capacities up to 2,000 gpm.

The World Class vehicles from

FIRE ENGINES

*This 1978 American LaFrance combination is equipped with a Pitman snorkel. The rig runs in Miami, Florida.*

American LaFrance incorporate new developments in composite materials and modular construction. The composite body is lighter than aluminum and stronger than steel, yet cannot corrode or electrolyze. The line is available on custom or commercial chassis.

The Century 2000 custom line is the premier offering from American LaFrance. Featuring stainless steel modular construction for easy maintenance, repair, and replacement, these units are powered by a 350-hp Detroit Diesel turbo engines with Allison automatic transmissions. Cab options include four-door, seven-passenger or two-door, five-passenger styles. A typical delivery on a Century 2000 chassis is a quint with

*Hollywood, Florida, is the home of this 1978 American LaFrance Century.*

*A 1970 Mack Model C
Aerialscope is demonstrated
in this factory shot. The
elevating platform extends
to 75 feet.*

FIRE ENGINES

75-foot aerial ladder, 1,500-gpm 2-stage Hale or Twinflow centrifugal pump, 500-gallon water tank, 30-gallon foam tank, and 1,000 feet of 5-inch hose.

American LaFrance remains one of the best-known names in fire apparatus. In recent years, however, the parent company, Figgie International Inc., has faced liquidity problems. It is possible that as part of a restructuring at Figgie, American LaFrance will be sold.

*Mack.* Chassis sales for commercial rigs was always a big part of the fire apparatus business at Mack. The MB chassis proved popular for both Mack-built apparatus and commercial builders.

This 1954 American LaFrance tillered aerial was rebuilt in 1983 with a Mack tractor. Note the open jump seats behind the cab.

Orange County, Florida runs this 1974 Mack cab-forward 600 rig. Pumping capacity is 1,250 gpm.

In 1978, the MB line was phased out in favor of the new MC and MR series. These chassis are still quite popular with commercial builders. Mack continued to be a major supplier to FDNY throughout the 1970s. The one thousandth FDNY motorized pumper was 1,000-gpm Mack CF Series diesel. Forty more

1,000-gpm pumpers went to FDNY in 1979; another 74 were delivered in 1980 and another ten in 1981; six 2,000-gpm pumpers were delivered in 1979.

By 1980, Mack was in financial difficulties. The firm was rescued in 1983 when Renault, the automotive company owned by the French government,

This heavy-duty Mack Model R Firepower tanker pumps 750 gpm and carries 3,000 gallons of water. This sort of capacity is necessary in rural areas such as Hope Valley, Rhode Island, home of this rig.

This shiny Mack/Ward 79 rig was delivered to West Palm Beach, Florida, in 1989.

bought 45% of the stock. With business not much better in 1984, Mack ceased producing custom pumpers and provided chassis only. Mack-based apparatus remained in demand, however. More than a hundred Mack/Ward 79 1,000 gpm pumpers were purchased by New York between 1984 and 1989; tower ladders from Mack/Baker and rescue trucks from Mack/Saulsbury are all now on the FDNY roster.

Fire apparatus is just one fairly small part of the entire Mack Truck operation. In 1990, Mack was reportedly losing $20 million a month. Quality had slipped and productivity was low. Renault protected its investment by purchasing the remaining stock, selling off some

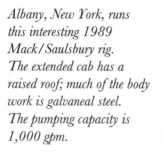

Albany, New York, runs this interesting 1989 Mack/Saulsbury rig. The extended cab has a raised roof; much of the body work is galvaneal steel. The pumping capacity is 1,000 gpm.

divisions, cutting the work force, and improving quality. Today Mack is in somewhat better financial condition but still faces an uncertain future. Renault, and with it Mack, is likely to be privatized by the French government in the foreseeable future. What will happen to Mack when it returns to shareholder hands remains to be seen.

*Seagrave.* The snorkel concept was greeted eagerly at Seagrave. By 1961 the firm was offering aerial platforms in 65- and 85-foot lengths and continues to offer elevating platforms on custom and commercial chassis. A new line of custom cab-forward, diesel-powered apparatus came from Seagrave in 1972. Starting in 1992, Seagrave delivered the

*This 1987 1,000-gpm Seagrave rig is owned by the Chesterfield County, Virginia, fire department.*

*This Sutphen aerial tower from 1975 serves Orlando, Florida. It is designated Tower 10.*

144

*Striking in both color and appearance, this 1992 Sutphen rig is a tanker for the Columbia Engine Company of Spring Valley, New York. It has a pumping capacity of 1,500 gpm.*

*This 1993 Sutphen is built on an International (now Navistar) chassis. It has a 1,250-gpm pump and carries 500 gallons of water. This rig protects Columbus, Ohio.*

first 12 of 100 1,000-gpm pumpers to FDNY—the first Seagrave pumpers since 1934.

Seagrave has always been well-known for aerial ladders, and they remain a big part of the firm's business today. Seagrave claims to have built more aerial ladders than any other company. Between 1974 and 1991, Seagrave delivered 48 100-foot tillered aerials to FDNY. More recently, four Model RA-110 rigs went to FDNY. These aerials have 110-foot ladders mounted on the four-door Model LP chassis, with seating for seven. The wheelbase on the trucks is 247 inches,

*A 75-foot rear-mounted ladder and a 2,000-gpm pump are features of this 1992 Pierce Lance.*

*Pierce traditionally backs the pump panel in black, as shown in this photo of a 1994 Saber. This rig offers forward-facing seating for six, a 750-gallon water tank, 1,250-gpm two-stage pump, and 300-horsepower engine.*

while the outrigger spread is 16 feet.

*Sutphen.* Sutphen had been a minor manufacturer of fire apparatus since the 1890s. In 1963, the family-owned firm began offering an outstanding aerial tower of its own design mounted on commercial chassis. Today Sutphen aerial towers and ladders are found across the country. Sutphen offers the 70+ line, a combination pumper/ladder/platform, as well as custom designs.

*Pierce.* After many years of making bodies for other companies, Pierce Manufacturing Company, based in Appleton, Wisconsin, began offering its

Van Pelt of California built this sturdy-looking rig on an International Harvester chassis in 1964. It is still in service in Oakdale, California. After being merged into FMC in the late 1980s, Van Pelt is today no more.

own line of fire apparatus on commercial chassis in 1968. The new models were immediate hits. The Suburban was particularly popular with smaller departments. The Power Chief line was introduced in 1970. The Javelin line of rear-engined, front-wheel-drive fire engines came out in the late 1980s. The engine is located just forward of the rear axles.

This makes the cab not only more spacious (it can accommodate up to ten people), but also considerably quieter, as mandated by recent federal safety requirements. The more traditional Dash line from Pierce uses a hydraulic tilt cab. The Pierce Arrow pumper is a cab-forward model dating from the late 1980s and still quite popular today.

Recent new models from Pierce include the Saber and the Responder. The Saber offers seating for up to eight, an open tilt cab design, an Allison transmission and a Detroit Diesel engine with up to 300 hp. The Responder is a smaller rig with a 250-hp engine, automatic transmission, and pumping capacity of 1,000 gpm. The 4900 Series International chassis has bench seating for three. Available options include two- or four-door cabs, water tanks of varying sizes, and a choice of side- or top-mounted controls. In March, 1993, Pierce delivered its 5,000th chassis, a custom-built Pierce Arrow for Oxnard, California.

This great view shows a 1993 Bronto 111-foot heavy-duty articulating device. It is mounted on a Pierce chassis with 500-horsepower engine.

152

## A CHANGING MARKETPLACE

The late 1980s and early 1990s saw some interesting changes in the fire apparatus marketplace.

FMC acquired Van Pelt, a California builder with a good regional following, in 1978. The operation was moved to FMC's Tipton, Indiana plant in 1987; shortly after this, FMC moved production to Orlando, Florida. By then, however, FMC was not doing well with fire apparatus. Management claimed that a turnaround was possible, but FMC has recently withdrawn from the fire apparatus business.

A merger in 1974 brought Howe and Oren Roanoake together; another merger added Coast Apparatus Company to the Howe group the same year. Howe continued making fire apparatus under its own name until the late 1980s, when the firm was merged into Grumman Emergency Products. Grumman offered some interesting products, including the Aerialcat 121-foot aerial ladder, but today the firm no longer produces fire apparatus.

In Canada, a number of fire apparatus companies have been successful as dealers and manufacturers, often building on American-made chassis. Superior Emergency Equipment of Alberta, for example, is now owned by Emergency One. Other modern Canadian producers include Hub Fire Engines of British Columbia, Anerson's Engineering of British Columbia, Almonte Fire Trucks of Ontario, and Dependable Emergency Vehicles of Ontario. A few companies have gone under in the late 1980s and early 1990s, including Thibault, Phoenix, Pierreville, and King Seagrave.

In the aerial platform business, new players such as Simon-LTI, Simon Dudley, and Simon-Duplex have been successful competitors to Snorkel Economy and others since the 1970s. The Skyarm from Nova Quintech in Quebec is a new articulating aerial platform; the Bronto Skylift is a telescoping articulating ladder platform.

A major success story dating from the mid-1970s is Emergency One, based in Ocala, Florida. A division of the well-known Federal Signal Company, E-One has grown rapidly and now holds a prominent place in the industry. The basis for the firm's success has been its pioneering use of heavy-duty extruded aluminum and aluminum plate for body construction. Strong, rigid, and light (about one-third lighter than steel), aluminum is also far less subject to corrosion—all qualities that make it particularly well suited to fire apparatus. To date, more than 12,000 Emergency One vehicles are in service worldwide.

The Hush series from Emergency One is a rear-engined chassis meant to reduce noise in the passenger compartment. E-One was the first to offer the rear-engine design. E-One has also built the tallest aerial in America. Constructed on an integrated box chassis that provides an extremely rigid frame, this aerial is 135 feet tall.

Starting in 1992, Emergency One has been offering the Rockwell Abco antilock braking system (ABS) as an option on all custom chassis.

One of the newest players in the fire apparatus field is Firewolf Industries Inc. of Lakeland, Florida. Firewolf uses mechanically fastened extrusions, adhesively bonded aluminum plate, and high-impact, shock-absorbing cone bearings to build apparatus on both commercial and custom-built specialty chassis. Current offerings from Firewolf include Class A pumpers, attack pumpers, mobile water supply apparatus, aerial ladders, aerial platforms, water towers,

aircraft crash vehicles and hazmat vehicles.

## THE FUTURE

While the future looks uncertain for some of the best-known names in fire apparatus, the industry itself is the scene of healthy competition. Stiff federal safety guidelines mean that some old apparatus must be retrofitted or replaced. New technological developments such as composite materials allow for fire apparatus with greater strength and less weight. Larger, quieter, more comfortable cabs are being specified on most new apparatus. Computers can now

control the pump panel, and communications continue to improve rapidly. Antilock brakes are becoming available and should do a great deal to improve safety on wet or icy streets. On the other hand, increasingly tight municipal budgets mean less money for the fire service even as that service is called on to provide emergency medical support and hazmat functions. The apparatus industry must balance the need for improvement with the need to keep costs low and quality high. Both manufacturers and municipalities must consider the needs and be sure the balance tilts in favor of the safety of the firefighters and the communities they protect.

*This 1993 Emergency One Hush combination pumper is in service in Kitchener, Ontario. The pump capacity is 1,050 gpm; the ladder extends to 50 feet.*

FIRE ENGINES

*A Snorkel Economy Tele-Squrt combination aerial ladder and telescopic boom is mounted on a Pierce chassis in this 1990 photo.*

*A new player in fire apparatus game is Firewolf Industries, based in Lakeland, Florida. The rig shown here was built on a commercial Ford chassis with extended cab.*

FIRE ENGINES

# Index *Numbers in italics indicate illustrations.*